Olivia Johnston

Series Authors
Chris Barker and Libby Mitchell

Mega 3
WORKBOOK THREE

Contents

Unit 1	Sports	2
Unit 2	Transportation	10
Unit 3	Communications	20
Unit 4	Movies and plays	28
Unit 5	Farms and farm animals	38
Unit 6	Jobs	46
Unit 7	House contents	56
Unit 8	Illness and injury	64
Unit 9	Town and country	74
Unit 10	Eating out	82
	Test Paper	92

UNIT 1 Sports

Vocabulary

1 Match a word from Box A with a word from Box B and label the pictures of the sports equipment.

1  soccer cleats

2  _____

3  _____

4  _____

5  _____

6 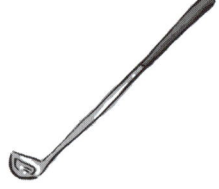 _____

7 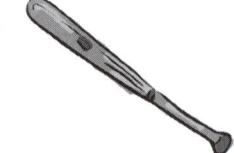 _____

8  _____

A
baseball   biking   ~~soccer~~   golf   football
skiing   swimming   tennis

B
skirt   shorts   jersey   goggles   trunks
club   ~~cleats~~   bat

Dialogue work

2 Complete the dialogue with the correct sentences.

Maddie Sit down, Jon.
Jon (1) _____
Maddie You're standing in front of the TV, and I can't see it.
Jon (2) _____
Maddie It's a sports show called *The Team*.
Jon (3) _____
Maddie I try to. But sometimes my friends don't let me.
Jon (4) _____
Maddie Well, sometimes my friends stand in front of the TV and talk.
Jon (5) _____
Maddie Er … so do I, Jon. Now, can you please sit down?
Jon (6) _____
Maddie Good.

- Sorry. I'm not going to say another word.
- Why?
- Who doesn't let you?
- What are you watching?
- I hate people like that.
- Do you watch it every week?

Grammar practice

3 Complete the sentences with the present tense of the verb *be*.

1 "_Are_ you Mexican?" "Yes, we _are_ ."
2 I'm not American. I _____ Australian.
3 Where _____ my shorts?
4 There's a pool near my house, but there _____ a tennis court.
5 I _____ very good at sports. I don't like getting hot and tired!
6 These _____ my goggles. They're yours.

4 Write sentences in the present simple using the correct verb from the box.

> play   do   go

1 How often / you / soccer?
How often do you play soccer?

2 I / swimming once a week
_____

3 your sister / track and field?
_____

4 They / baseball a lot in the USA
_____

5 Ellen / not / a lot of sports
_____

6 your sisters / bike riding in the park?
_____

7 Which day / you and Joey / gymnastics?
_____

8 you / sometimes / volleyball on the beach?
_____

5 Match the sentences and responses. Then write them in the present continuous.

1 Shh! I _'m watching_ (watch) the big game on TV.
☐ c _Who's playing?_

2 _____ (you / feel) okay?
☐ _____

3 _____ (Jon / eat) again?
☐ _____

4 _____ (we / win)?
☐ _____

5 Zoe _____ (not play) very well.
☐ _____

a) No, we (lose), I'm afraid.
b) She (do) her best.
~~c) Who (play)?~~
d) Yes, he (have) a sandwich!
e) Yes, I (feel) better now, thanks.

6 Use the diary to write Carmela's plans for next week in the present continuous.

1 **Monday**	Gymnastics with Sonia. Then have lunch together.
2 **Tuesday**	Tennis with Rosie. Meet her at the tennis court.
3 **Wednesday**	Stay at home. Help Mom with the housework.
4 **Thursday**	Get up early. Pick up Katie from the airport.

1 _On Monday, I'm doing gymnastics with Sonia. Then we're having lunch together._

2 _____

3 _____

4 _____

7 Complete the sentences with a verb from the list in the present continuous. Then write *P* (present) or *F* (future) next to each sentence.

hold ~~look at~~ read run visit watch

1 Why _are_ you _looking at_ me like that? Are you angry? [P]
2 _____ you _____ in the 800-meter race or the 500-meter?
3 Please be quiet. I _____ a really exciting story.
4 We _____ my cousins in Cincinnati next weekend.
5 _____ you _____ *The Simpsons* on TV tonight?
6 Why _____ you _____ my socks like that? Do they smell?

8 Respond to these statements using *So ...* or *Neither ...* .

1 I'm always late for my dance class.
   _So am_ I.
2 My parents don't like rap music.
   Neither do mine.
3 We're going to the beach on the weekend.
   _____ I.
4 I don't know any good shoe shops.
   _____ I.
5 Your socks are really dirty.
   _____ yours.
6 I don't eat meat.
   _____ we.
7 Sandra's really good at languages.
   _____ you.
8 My dog loves his food.
   _____ my cat.
9 I'm carrying two bags.
   _____ Fred.
10 You aren't helping.
   _____ Max.

9 Circle the correct form, and write *PC* (present continuous) or *PS* (present simple) in the box.

1 Be quiet! Who *makes / is making* that horrible noise? [PC]
2 We often *go / are going* for picnics on the beach in the summer.
3 "What's that music?" "My mother *plays / is playing* one of her strange CDs!"
4 *Do you wear / Are you wearing* a uniform at your school?
5 You *don't wear / aren't wearing* your glasses today.
6 What *do you do / are you doing* with that bag of candy?
7 Sometimes we *win / are winning*, but not always.
8 Be careful! You *stand / are standing* on my jacket.

10 Put the verbs in the present simple or the present continuous.

1 How often _do you go_ (you / go) swimming?
2 Look! Gianni _is running_ (run) across the field.
3 What _____ (you / do) with my shoes?
4 What time _____ (you / get up) on Saturdays?
5 Excuse me, I _____ (look) for the library.
6 Jeremy _____ (do) sports three times a week.
7 At the moment, we _____ (study) volcanoes in Geography.
8 My father _____ (run) four kilometers every day.
9 Why _____ (you / carry) those chairs to the backyard?
10 In this photo, Tara _____ (wear) her grandmother's hat.

11 What are their New Year's resolutions? Complete the sentences using *going to* and the correct phrase from the box.

> work out every day   read lots of books
> save up for a camera   ~~go for a walk every day~~
> be kind to my brother   learn another language

In the U.S., people often make New Year's resolutions on January 1. They decide to change their life in some way, for example, by always finishing their weekend homework by Friday evening.

1 Next year, I <u>am going to go for a walk every day.</u>

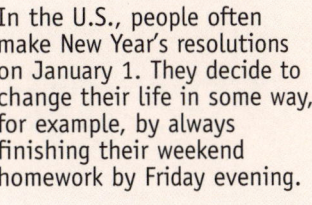

2 Next year, I _____ _____ _____

3 Next year, I _____ _____ _____

4 Next year, I _____ _____ _____

5 Next year, I _____ _____ _____

6 Next year, I _____ _____ _____

12 Complete sentences 1–5 with *going to*, and sentences 6–10 with the present continuous.

1 Hurry up! We <u>'re going to miss</u> (miss) the plane.
2 He doesn't know about it. Who _____ _____ (tell) him?
3 "You have chocolate on your dress." "I know. I _____ (clean) it in a minute."
4 I don't have any money. How _____ _____ (pay) for my sandwich?
5 Rodman has the ball. He _____ (score) another goal.
6 What <u>are you doing</u> (you / do) at ten o'clock tomorrow?
7 My friends from Brazil _____ (arrive) at three o'clock.
8 Sorry, I can't stay. I _____ (meet) Jon at the gym in five minutes.
9 Why _____ (they leave) on Saturday?
10 I _____ (play) tennis with Sara at three o'clock tomorrow.

UNIT 1   5

UNIT 1 Skills Development

Lewis Hadley's ambition is to be a professional tennis player. "Tennis is the most important thing in my life," he says. "I want to play tennis at Wimbledon one day."

Fourteen-year-old Lewis goes to Central High School in Pasadena, California. (1) *His favorite subjects are English and Math.* He's a good student, and he's doing well at school, but for Lewis, life begins after school. At four o'clock, (2) _____ , he bikes to the tennis court and plays tennis for two hours. His **coach**, Richard Dellinger, is **pleased** with Lewis's **progress**. "(3) _____ . He's playing excellent tennis this year. And in my opinion, he has the right **character** to be a tennis **champion**. When he makes a **mistake**, he doesn't **lose** his head. He doesn't get upset, and (4) _____ . He's very **controlled**."

Lewis watches a lot of tennis videos. "(5) _____ ," he says. "I love watching Lleyton Hewitt and Marat Safin. They're two of the best players at the moment." He also loves watching **live** tennis matches. "We're going to go to the Men's Finals at Wimbledon in England this year. (6) _____ . I can't wait. The **atmosphere** at Wimbledon is really **exciting**."

Lewis's other passion in life is photography. "I have a **digital** camera. It's fantastic. You don't need to put film in the camera. I take pictures and **download** them onto my computer. Then I **keep** the good pictures and **delete** the bad ones. Right now, I'm taking a lot of pictures of people—(7) _____ . It's interesting. I like watching people."

Reading

1 Read the magazine article. Where should these sentences go? Write them in the correct spaces.

- he doesn't get angry
- ~~His favorite subjects are English and Math~~
- I learn a lot from them
- in the park, on the street, on the bus
- Lewis is doing very well
- My dad already has the plane tickets
- after school

2 Read the text again and write down the meaning of these words and phrases. If you don't know them, guess and then check in a dictionary or with your teacher.

1	coach	_____	N
2	pleased	_____	___
3	progress	_____	___
4	character	_____	___
5	champion	_____	___
6	mistake	_____	___
7	lose	_____	___
8	controlled	_____	___
9	live	_____	___
10	atmosphere	_____	___
11	exciting	_____	___
12	digital	_____	___
13	download	_____	___
14	keep	_____	___
15	delete	_____	___

Study Tip

3 When you look words up in the dictionary, it is useful to know what kinds of words they are. Look at the words in Exercise 2 again and write *N* (noun), *V* (verb), or *Adj* (adjective) next to each word.

Listening

4 Listen and look at the photos. Which photo does Lewis keep? Check (✔) the box.

a ☐

b ☐

c ☐

d ☐

Writing

5 Write about someone in your class who already knows what she/he wants to be one day. Use these sentences to help you.

_____'s ambition is to be a _____ . "_____ is the most important thing in my life," he/she says. "I want to _____ one day." _____-year-old _____ _____ goes to school in _____ . His/Her favorite subjects are _____ and _____ . She's/He's a good student, and she's/he's doing well at school. She/He also enjoys _____ and _____ . When he/she graduates high school, he/she is going to _____ . Then she/he hopes to _____ .

UNIT 1

Talk time

1 Write the phrases in the correct balloons.

- Great hit!
- Good catch!
- Good luck!
- See you there.
- Be quiet!

Let's Check

Vocabulary check

1 Complete the sentences with *go, do,* or *play* and a sports location word.

1. Let's <u>go</u> to the stock car races. There's a <u>racetrack</u> near my house.
2. Do you want to _____ gymnastics? There's a good class at the _____ on Central Avenue.
3. Let's _____ tennis after lunch. There's a _____ in the park.
4. We're going to _____ soccer on the _____ near Dan's house.
5. I can't _____ track and field right now because the _____ is closed.
6. Let's _____ swimming. There's a new _____ on Market Street.

Grammar check

2 Correct the mistake in each sentence.

◆ = there's a word missing
N = change the order of two words
X = change one word
* = delete one word

1. What you looking at? ◆
   <u>What are you looking at?</u>
2. I go usually swimming on Sundays. **N**
   _____
3. Are you going buy the new Shakira CD? ◆
   _____
4. My sister doesn't playing in the game on Saturday. **X**
   _____
5. You always are late for football practice. **N**
   _____
6. I don't like hockey and so neither does Luke. *
   _____

3 Choose the correct words for each sentence.

1. "I do a lot of sports." "So ____."
   A I do   B am I   **C do I** (circled)
2. "They aren't going to have a soda." "Neither ____."
   A am I   B I am   C do I
3. ____ you meeting them at six?
   A Do   B Will   C Are
4. "Rose doesn't eat meat." "____ Tom."
   A So does   B Neither does   C Neither is
5. I ____ tennis every day next week.
   A playing   B play   C am going to play
6. "Jack is very musical." "____ you."
   A Neither are   B So are   C So do
7. I don't have any money. How am I ____ home?
   A getting   B going to get   C get
8. "My brother loves motorcycles." "____ mine."
   A So is   B Neither does   C So does
9. What ____ to the party?
   A you wear   B do you wear   C are you wearing
10. "My racket isn't here." "____ mine."
    A Neither are   B So is   C Neither is
11. Come on! We're ____ the bus.
    A missing   B going to miss   C to miss

4 Make sentences by putting the words in order.

1. I'm / me / my / swimsuit / taking / this / weekend / with
   <u>I'm taking my swimsuit with me this weekend.</u>
2. are / balls / do / going / old / tennis / the / to / What / with / you / ?
   _____
3. beach / coming / isn't / Josie / on / party / Saturday / the / to
   _____
4. an / are / e-mail / Mr. Kent / to / Why / writing / you / ?
   _____
5. and so / he / is / I'm / new / sneakers / wearing
   _____

UNIT **1**   **9**

UNIT 2 Transportation

Vocabulary

1 Use the pictures to complete the crossword.

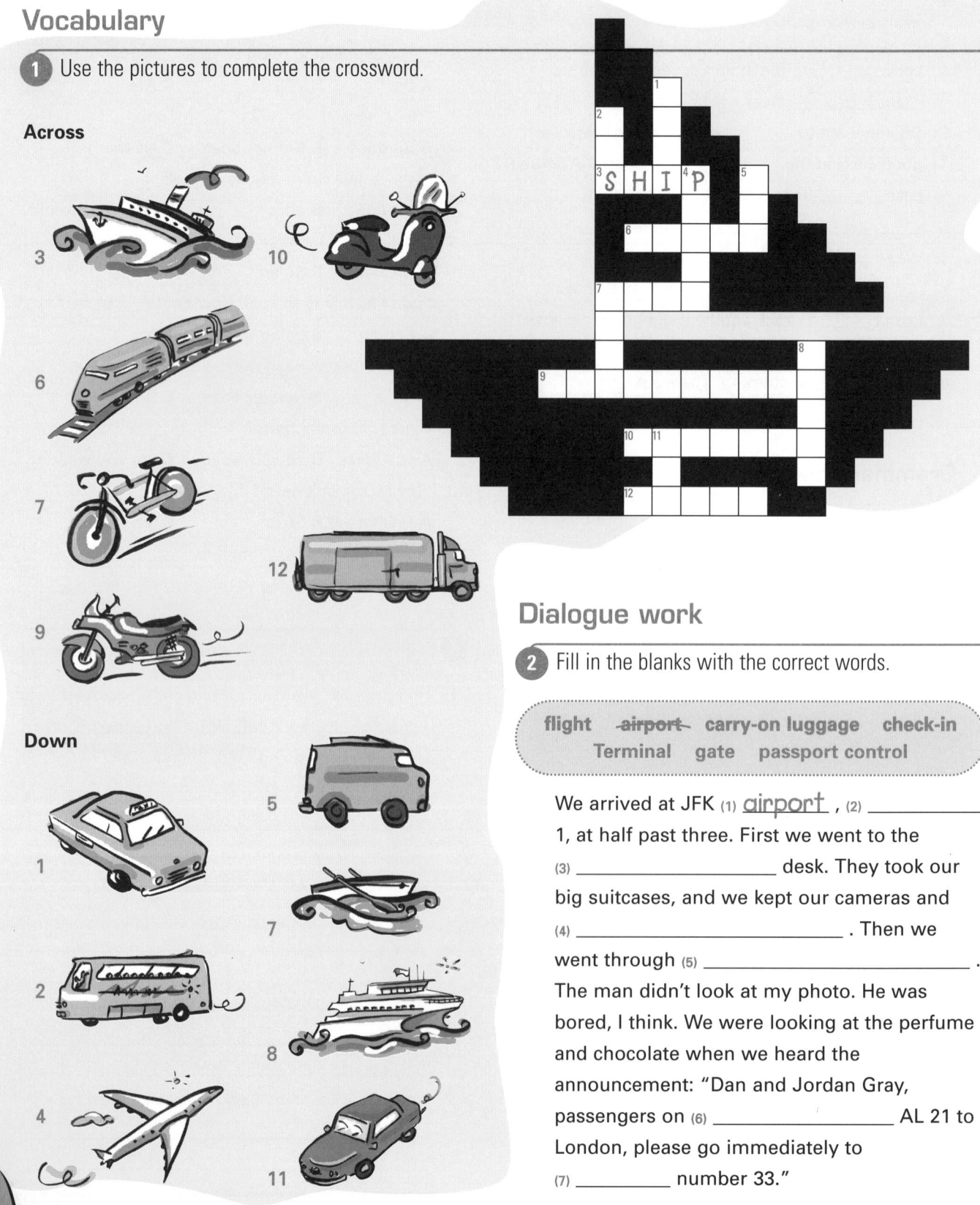

Across
3, 10, 6, 7, 9

Down
1, 5, 7, 2, 8, 4, 11, 12

Dialogue work

2 Fill in the blanks with the correct words.

> flight   ~~airport~~   carry-on luggage   check-in
> Terminal   gate   passport control

We arrived at JFK (1) <u>airport</u>, (2) _____ 1, at half past three. First we went to the (3) _____ desk. They took our big suitcases, and we kept our cameras and (4) _____. Then we went through (5) _____. The man didn't look at my photo. He was bored, I think. We were looking at the perfume and chocolate when we heard the announcement: "Dan and Jordan Gray, passengers on (6) _____ AL 21 to London, please go immediately to (7) _____ number 33."

3 Complete the dialogue with the sentences below.

Rachel Come on, Maddie. Let's go and buy some presents.
Maddie (1) _I have to find my passport first._
Rachel Where did you put it?
Maddie (2) _____
Rachel Did you give it to Mike?
Maddie (3) _____
Rachel Don't panic. We'll find it. We won't leave you in Italy!
Maddie (4) _____
Rachel I have an idea. Look in your suitcase. I bet it's there.
Maddie (5) _____
Rachel You probably packed it with your clothes. Now, let's go.
Maddie (6) _____
Rachel Now what's the problem?
Maddie (7) _____

- Amazing! How did it get in there?
- Aaarh! Oh, where is it?
- Did I give you my purse?
- ~~I have to find my passport first.~~
- No, I didn't. I had it in my hand a minute ago.
- That's the problem. I don't know.
- Er ... can you wait a minute?

Grammar practice

4 Complete the sentences about their jobs. Use *has to / have to* or *doesn't have to / don't have to*.

singer
1. She _has to_ have a good voice.
2. She _doesn't have to_ speak a lot of languages.
3. She often _has to_ work at night.

soccer players
4. They _____ practice a lot.
5. They _____ be good at Math.
6. They _____ travel.
7. They _____ use a computer.

bus driver
8. She _____ wear a uniform.
9. She _____ work at night.
10. She _____ know the town.
11. She _____ enjoy driving.

school teacher
12. He _____ like children.
13. He _____ work at night.
14. He _____ travel.
15. He _____ stand a lot.

UNIT 2

5 Complete the sentences with the correct form of *have to* and a verb from the box.

> be   bike   ~~get up~~   learn   take   wear

1 My father _has to get up_ at 6:30 on weekdays to be at work by 8:00.
2 I'm tired, Mom. _____ I _____ the dog for a walk?
3 _____ your sister _____ a uniform at her school?
4 In the U.S., all children _____ Math at school.
5 My friend Justin _____ to school now. He has a new scooter, lucky thing.
6 Sandra's parents are really strict. She _____ home by nine o'clock on Saturday night.

6 Complete the sentences with *shouldn't* or *doesn't have to / don't have to*.

1 You _shouldn't_ go swimming after a big meal. It's dangerous.
2 It's Sunday tomorrow, so she _doesn't have to_ get up early. She can stay in bed until 11:00.
3 He _____ pay. I have a free ticket for him.
4 They _____ make any noise. Ben is sleeping.
5 We _____ join after-school clubs, but we all like being in them.
6 There's lots of time. We _____ run to the bus stop.
7 You _____ tell Maria. It's our secret, okay?
8 She can bring a friend to the party, but she _____ .
9 Take those dirty soccer cleats off. You _____ wear them in the house.

7 What do you have to do at home? Write three sentences about things you have to do and three sentences about things you don't have to do.

I have to take the dog for walks.
I don't have to cook dinner.
_____
_____
_____
_____
_____
_____
_____
_____
_____
_____

8 Complete the e-mail with the correct form of the past simple of the verb *be*.

> **Send Mail: Message Composition**
>
> Hi Luke,
> Where (1) _were_ you at six o'clock? I called you, but you (2) _____ in. How (3) _____ your vacation? Mine (4) _____ great. The food (5) _____ excellent. The beaches (6) _____ great, and the girls (7) _____ beautiful. The first day, there (8) _____ any sun, but after that the weather (9) _____ perfect. We (10) _____ in a hotel by the sea. The view from my window (11) _____ amazing. There (12) _____ only one problem. There (13) _____ any tennis courts. (14) _____ your exam results okay? Mine (15) _____ too bad. My parents (16) _____ pretty pleased with me for a change!
> Ciao for now,
> Dan

9 Complete the e-mail with the past simple of the verbs.

Send Mail: Message Composition

Hi Dan,
I (1) _got_ (get) back from South Carolina this morning and (2) _____ (find) your e-mail. Good news about the exams, man. I (3) _____ (do) okay, too. I (4) _____ (have) a great vacation camping in Pawleys Island. I (5) _____ (go) with Sam and Noah. In the end, Jack (6) _____ (not come) with us. We (7) _____ (stay) at a campground on the beach. We (8) _____ (meet) some girls from Virginia and (9) _____ (spend) a lot of time with them. The weather (10) _____ (not be) very good, but at least it (11) _____ (not rain). Sam and I (12) _____ (cook) in the evenings. I (13) _____ (make) spaghetti once, but it (14) _____ (take) hours! Next time I'm buying it in cans. Noah (15) _____ (not want) to cook, so he (16) _____ (have to) do the dishes every night! We (17) _____ (not sleep) very much at night. We (18) _____ (sit) around on the beach and (19) _____ (talk) for hours. (20) _____ (you / meet) any nice girls in California? What (21) _____ (you / do) there in the evenings? (22) _____ (you / go) surfing there? When (23) _____ (you get) back?
Hope to C U soon.
Luke

Study Tip

Practicing the past simple

Before each English lesson, practice using the past simple by asking a friend:
What did you do last night?

Your friend has to tell you three things, for example:
I got the bus into town.
I went to the movies.
I had ice cream.

10 Complete the sentences in the past continuous.

1 You _were laughing_ (laugh) in your sleep last night.
2 What _____ (you / do) yesterday at three o'clock?
3 _____ (she / wear) her new earrings at Jade's party?
4 We _____ (not talk) about you. We _____ (talk) about Tracy's cousin.
5 It _____ (not rain) at ten o'clock this morning.
6 Why _____ (Jacob write) in his diary at six o'clock this morning?
7 He _____ (not write) in it. He _____ (draw) a picture of his surfboard!

11 Put the verbs in the past simple or the past continuous.

Last year, I (1) _was staying_ (stay) with my friend Megan in New York. Her house is very old. One night, I (2) _____ (read) in bed. Suddenly I (3) _____ (hear) a boy's voice. The boy (4) _____ (sing) an old song called *Greensleeves*. I (5) _____ (get) out of bed and (6) _____ (open) the door of my room. There was nobody there. In the morning, I (7) _____ (ask) Megan, "(8) _____ (you / sing) in the middle of the night?" "No," she said. "Why? (9) _____ (you / hear) a boy singing *Greensleeves*?" "Yes," I (10) _____ (answer). "Who is he?" "That's our ghost," she said. "His name is Tom. He (11) _____ (die) in your bedroom a hundred years ago."

CULTURE SPOT

CHARLES DICKENS

In the 19th century, English people loved novels. There were lots of bookstores and libraries, and people had plenty of time to read. Some novelists wrote their books in episodes. People bought one episode a month. It was cheaper than buying a whole book.

Charles Dickens (1812–1870) wrote novels in this way. He ended each episode with something very exciting so people wanted to buy the next episode. He became the most popular novelist of his time. His books were exciting and funny, but they also had a lot of serious messages. He often wrote about poor people and their difficult lives. When people read Dickens's books, they began to understand the problems of the poor.

Charles Dickens knew about the lives of poor people because his own family was poor. His father was in prison for six months because he didn't have enough money to pay his bills. Charles went to work in a shoe-polish factory when he was only twelve.

Oliver Twist is one of Dickens's most famous novels. Oliver Twist lives in an orphanage because he doesn't have any parents. The orphanage is cold, and the children are hungry. When Oliver asks for more food, he gets in a lot of trouble. He leaves the orphanage and goes to London. He meets a man named Fagin. Fagin has a group of children who take money and jewelry from people on the street. Then Fagin keeps the money and the jewelry. Oliver doesn't want to work for him, but he has to. Oliver has a lot of adventures, but the story has a happy ending.

1 _____

2 _____

3 _____

Dickens also wrote *A Christmas Carol*. It's the story of a very mean man named Scrooge. He pays his workers really badly. Even at Christmas, he doesn't give them extra money. One of his workers is named Bob Cratchit. His son, Tiny Tim, is sick and can't walk. The Cratchit family has a very hard life. Then on Christmas Eve, three ghosts visit Scrooge. He is very scared, and he changes. He starts to be kind and generous, and he gives presents to everyone. Today, we still call a mean person "a scrooge."

Reading

1 Read the text about Charles Dickens, then write the captions under the correct pictures.

- Scrooge sees one of the ghosts.
- Charles Dickens wrote very popular novels.
- Oliver asks for more food in the orphanage.

2 Write short answers to the questions.

1 When was Dickens born? <u>1812</u>
2 When did he die? _____
3 Why didn't people buy complete books in those days?
   _____
4 Why did Dickens's father have problems?
   _____
   _____
5 How old was Dickens when he got his first job?
   _____
6 Why does Oliver get into trouble at the orphanage?
   _____
7 Who does Bob Cratchit work for?
   _____
8 Who is Tiny Tim? _____
9 What does Scrooge see on Christmas Eve?
   _____

Vocabulary

3 Find the words in the text for the following.

1 a period of 100 years <u>century</u>
2 a type of book _____
3 a person who writes this type of book _____
4 a part of a story _____
5 the opposite of funny _____
6 the opposite of rich _____
7 something for cleaning shoes _____
8 a place for children who have no family _____
9 the opposite of generous _____
10 the night before Christmas _____

Project

4 Write about you and reading.

- Do you prefer reading books or magazines?
- What's your favorite book of all time?
- Do you buy books or borrow them?
- What kind of books do you like best? *(Novels? Books about science/sports/ famous people/history?)*
- How do you usually choose your books? *(Look at the pictures? Copy friends? Read a few pages?)*
- When do you usually read? *(In bed? On the weekends?)*
- What was the last book you read?
- What was it like?

_____
_____
_____
_____
_____
_____
_____
_____
_____
_____
_____
_____
_____
_____
_____
_____
_____
_____
_____
_____
_____

Listening

1 What did they think of *Oliver Twist*? Listen and write the correct letter in each box.

Welcome to the Book Club

a) It was hard.
b) It was exciting.
c) It was funny.
d) ~~It was interesting.~~
e) It was terrible.
f) It was too long.
g) It was scary.

1 Sara — d
2 Lucy — ☐
3 Dan — ☐
4 Ben — ☐
5 Amy — ☐

2 Amy is talking about reading. Listen and check (✔) the correct boxes.

	True	False
1 Amy prefers novels.	✔	
2 She gets most of her books at a local bookstore.		
3 She can borrow books free at her local library.		
4 She chooses books by looking at the pictures in them.		
5 She reads every day.		
6 She saw the movie of *Lord of the Rings* first, then read the book.		

Let's Check

Vocabulary check

1 Match the transportation words to the sentences.

> bike boat cab car bus truck
> motorcycle plane ~~ship~~ train

1 It travels across the sea. __ship__
2 It goes on roads. You have to have a ticket to travel on it. _____
3 You get on it at an airport. _____
4 Children can ride it. _____
5 It carries heavy boxes and other things on roads. _____
6 It's smaller than a ship. _____
7 It's another word for a taxi. _____
8 Only one or two people can go on it. _____
9 It goes on tracks. You get on it at a station. _____
10 Most families have one. _____

Grammar check

2 Choose the correct words for each sentence.

1 We ___ his passport in the car yesterday.
   A find   **B found**   C finding
2 She doesn't ___ go by bus. She can take the train.
   A have to   B need   C should
3 They should ___ make a noise.
   A not   B have   C to
4 I ___ score a goal.
   A wasn't   B haven't   C didn't
5 You ___ me perfume last summer.
   A buy   B were buying   C bought
6 What ___ for breakfast yesterday?
   A had you   B you had   C did you have
7 They ___ upset about the game.
   A were   B was   C did
8 Who were you ___ to after the movie yesterday?
   A talked   B talking   C talk
9 "I wrote to Emma today." "So ___ Joey."
   A do   B was   C did
10 I have ___ the dog for a walk now.
   A to take   B taking   C take
11 My dad ___ delicious pancakes for breakfast.
   A make   B made   C making

3 Correct the mistake in each sentence.

> ◆ = there's a word missing
> **N** = change the order of two words
> **X** = change one word
> * = delete one word

1 I have buy a present for my sister. ◆
   __I have to buy a present for my sister.__
2 We don't have to going yet. **X**
   _____
3 What do we have do for homework? ◆
   _____
4 Who you were waiting for at the café? **N**
   _____
5 Who did drew this picture in my notebook? *
   _____
6 I didn't found any nice chocolates in that shop. **X**
   _____

4 Make sentences by putting the words in order.

1 airport / arrived / and / at / check-in desk / to / the / the / We / went
   __We arrived at the airport and went__
   __to the check-in desk.__
2 Do / have / I / in / game / on / play / Saturday / the / to / ?
   _____
3 bed / did / dirty / soccer / leave / my / on / jersey / you / your / Why / ?
   _____
4 but / call / have / her / to Kim / should / to write / you / You don't
   _____
5 a / bird / huge / I / I / on / saw / walking / the / beach / was / when
   _____
6 a call / got / I / I / cell / my / on / phone / the / game / while / was / watching
   _____

UNIT 2

The Brontës

Jane Eyre and Wuthering Heights are two of the most popular novels in English literature. Jane Eyre is by Charlotte Brontë, and Wuthering Heights is the work of her sister Emily.

The six Brontë children grew up in the small village of Haworth in Yorkshire, England. Their father, Patrick, was a Church of England priest in Haworth. Their mother, Maria, died in 1821, when the oldest child was only seven.

A few years after their mother's death, the four oldest girls went to a church boarding school. It was a terrible experience and ended in disaster. The school was cold, the food was bad, and the teachers were very strict. Eleven-year-old Maria and ten-year-old Elizabeth Brontë became very ill. Their father brought the four girls home, but Maria and Elizabeth never got better. They died of tuberculosis a few months later.

From 1824 to 1831, the four surviving Brontë children, Charlotte, Branwell (the only boy), Emily, and Anne, stayed at home and had classes with their father and their aunt. They didn't have friends outside their home, and they didn't meet the children in the village. It was a very quiet life, but the children were close to each other in age, and they loved using their imagination. They enjoyed reading and wrote little books in tiny writing for Branwell's toy soldiers to read.

Later on, the three girls worked as teachers. Charlotte and Anne were private teachers to the children of rich families. Then, for a short time, Charlotte and Emily taught at a girls' school in Brussels. None of them enjoyed teaching, and, when their aunt died and left them some money, they decided to stay at their family home, writing.

Charlotte's Jane Eyre, Emily's Wuthering Heights, and Anne's Agnes Grey were published in 1847. But the Brontë family didn't have long to celebrate. In 1848, Branwell died of tuberculosis. Nine months later, Emily and Anne were dead of the same illness.

Jane Eyre was a great success. Charlotte Brontë made a lot of money from it and became pretty famous. She wrote several more novels before marrying in 1854. Tragically, she died a year later at the age of 39.

The Brontës' house in Haworth is now a museum. You can see the dining room where the three young women spent their evenings discussing the characters and plots of their novels and doing their writing. And you can get an idea of the everyday life of this very unusual family.

Reading

1 Read the text and answer the questions.

1. Who wrote *Wuthering Heights*?
   _____
2. How many children were there in the Brontë family?
   _____
3. Where did they live?
   _____
4. What was the church boarding school like?
   _____
   _____
5. At what age did Maria and Elizabeth Brontë die?
   _____
   _____
6. How many brothers did the Brontë sisters have?
   _____
7. Who taught the Brontë children after Maria and Elizabeth's deaths?
   _____
   _____
8. How did the Brontë sisters get enough money to stop working as teachers?
   _____
   _____
9. What is the Brontës' house now?
   _____
10. In which room did the Brontës write their novels?
    _____
    _____
11. What is your favorite book? Write two sentences saying what it's about.
    _____
    _____
    _____
12. Do you prefer books or movies? Why?
    _____
    _____

Writing

2 Complete your part of the dialogue.

Interviewer I'm writing an article for a magazine. Can I ask you a few questions?
You *Yes, of course.*
Interviewer What kinds of things do you have to do to help at home?
You _____
_____
Interviewer Really? So you have to do a lot. And how long does it take you to do the dishes every evening?
You _____
Interviewer Are there any jobs you hate doing?
You _____
Interviewer I don't like doing that, either! How often do you have to do that?
You _____
_____
Interviewer How much allowance do you get a week?
You _____
Interviewer That's a lot! What do you spend it on?
You _____
_____
Interviewer And after all that, do you manage to save any of it?
You _____
_____
Interviewer What are you saving up for?
You _____
_____
Interviewer So who are you going to go with on this trip?
You _____
_____
Interviewer Thanks very much for your time.

UNIT 3 Communications

Vocabulary

1 Use the pictures to complete the crossword.

Across

1

4

6

9

Down

2

3

5

8

7

2 Complete the entries in the chart for yourself.

My zip code	
My e-mail address	
My cell-phone number	
Emergency services	
Directory assistance	
International code for my country	
Emergency services in the U.S.	9-1-1

20 UNIT 3

Dialogue work

3 Complete the dialogue with the words from the box.

> card   envelope   Europe   kisses   letter
> photo   post office   ~~stamps~~

Adam Do you have any (1) _stamps_ ?
Maddie I have one. Who have you written to?
Adam Do I have to tell you?
Maddie Yes, if you want this stamp.
Adam Well, I've made a (2) _____ for my grandma. It's her birthday tomorrow.
Maddie Okay. Here you go.
Adam Thanks. Now I need a stamp for (3) _____ for my letter to Tommaso. I suppose I'll have to go to the (4) _____ .
Maddie Have you closed the (5) _____ ?
Adam No.
Maddie Can you put this (6) _____ of me and Rachel in with your (7) _____ ?
Adam Okay.
Maddie Who's the third letter to?
Adam Eloisa.
Maddie Let me see.
Adam What?
Maddie That's funny. You haven't put any (8) _____ on the envelope.

Grammar practice

4 Put the verbs in the present perfect. They are all regular.

1 I _have tried_ (try) all the pizzas on this menu. Pizza Surprise is the best.
2 Elly _____ (save) a lot of money. She's going to buy a camera.
3 My aunt _____ (move) to a new house. She lives in Pensacola now.
4 They _____ (decide) to go live in Spain.
5 She's really annoyed because somebody _____ (open) her letter from Dan.
6 We _____ (listen) to all the songs on this CD. The one called *Sweet Kisses* is the best.
7 She _____ (look) everywhere, but she still can't find her passport.
8 Justin _____ (invite) 30 people to his barbecue. It will be fun.
9 I _____ (start) this book three times, but I always get bored at page 20!
10 My sister _____ (join) a movie club. She gets very cheap movie tickets now.
11 I _____ (change) my e-mail address. I'll give you my new one.

5 Write the correct verb in each blank in the present perfect. They are all irregular.

> cut   do   buy   go   ~~make~~
> lose   meet   see   eat

1 We _'ve made_ some popcorn. Would you like some?
2 I _____ all my homework. I'm going out now.
3 She _____ that movie twice. She doesn't want to see it again.
4 We can't make sandwiches. Fred _____ all the bread and cheese.
5 You _____ my English uncle. His name is George.
6 Luke _____ the keys. How are we going to get into the house?
7 Phillip can't be in the race. He _____ his foot and he can't run.
8 Her parents _____ to Australia. They're coming back in February.
9 My dad _____ me a new tennis racket. It's great!

UNIT 3

6 Choose the correct prompts and complete the responses in the present perfect.

1. Does Sylvie like her new school?
   I don't know because <u>she hasn't written to me.</u>
2. Are Tim and Andy having fun in Toronto?
   Probably, but _____
   _____
3. We got a postcard from Rosie.
   Lucky you! _____
4. Does your mom like the books?
   She says so, but _____
   _____
5. What was the cake like?
   We don't know. _____
6. What do you think of Dan's cousins?
   I don't know. _____

- I (not meet) them
- she (not read) them all
- ~~she (not write) to me.~~
- she (not send) us one.
- we (not hear) from them
- we (not try) it

7 Match the statements to the questions. Write the questions in the present perfect.

1. It's Selina's birthday tomorrow. [b]
   What <u>have you bought her?</u>
2. I'm going out with Lily now, Mom. ☐
   _____
   _____
3. Can you lend me your glasses for a minute? ☐
   _____
4. We can probably have the party at Jamie's. ☐
   _____
5. Ben's back at school now. ☐
   _____
6. Carly doesn't live in Kansas City now. ☐
   _____

> There are two present perfect forms for the verb go: *have/has gone* and *have/has been*.
> - We use *have/has gone* when the person has gone somewhere and has not returned.
>   "Where's Gwyneth?"
>   "She's gone to the park."
> - We use *have/has been* when the person has made a visit and has now returned.
>   "Where have you been?"
>   "We've been to the movies."

8 Complete the sentences with the present perfect, using *been* or *gone*.

1. "Is Alex in?" "No, he isn't. He <u>'s gone</u> to a basketball game."
2. "You're late getting home. Where <u>have you been</u>?" "We <u>'ve been</u> to a party."
3. They _____ to Cancun. They'll be back in a week.
4. "What's China like?" "I don't know. I _____n't _____ there."
5. Sandro _____ to the beach. He'll be back around six o'clock.
6. "I want to go to New Orleans." "I _____ _____ there twice. It's a beautiful city."
7. You _____ to a lot of parties this week. Why don't you stay at home this evening?
8. The Redferns aren't here. They _____ on vacation.
9. Is Alisa here or _____ she _____ to soccer practice?

a) (he / be) sick?
b) ~~(you / buy) her?~~
c) (you / done) your homework, darling?
d) (you / lose) yours again?
e) (he / ask) his parents?
f) Where (she / move) to?

9 Write questions with *Have you ever* ... . Then answer them in your notebook.

ARE YOU CRAZY ABOUT PARTIES?

1. (invite) more than 40 people to a party?
2. (dance) on a table at a party?
3. (go) to a party in your pajamas?
4. (be) the last person to leave a party?
5. (have) three party invitations on the same night?
6. (make) a lot of noise at a party?
7. (stay) up all night at a party?
8. (fall) off a chair at a party?
9. (play) in a band at a party?
10. (lose) your shoes at a party?
11. (clean) the house after a party?

1 <u>Have you ever invited more than 40 people to a party? Yes, I have. / No, I haven't.</u>
2 ____
3 ____
4 ____
5 ____
6 ____
7 ____
8 ____
9 ____
10 ____
11 ____

10 Use the prompts to write sentences in the present perfect.

1 Josh (try) (✔) snowboarding (✘) surfing
<u>Josh has tried snowboarding, but he hasn't tried surfing.</u>

2 I (be) (✔) plane (✘) ship
____

3 You (write) (✔) a story (✘) song
____

4 I (work) (✔) in a café (✘) shop
____

5 I (go) (✔) to New York (✘) Boston
____

6 She (see) (✔) Andrea (✘) Sylvie
____

11 Complete the dialogues with the correct form of the present perfect.

A: (1) <u>Have you tried</u> (you / try) Silkilox shampoo?

B: No, I haven't, but I (2) _____ (see) the commercials on TV. Alice (3) _____ (use) it a few times.

A: (4) _____ (you / do) all the Spanish homework?

B: No, I (5) _____ . I (6) _____ (read) the questions, but I (7) _____ (not write) the answers.

A: Mina (8) _____ (not do) any work this year.

B: She doesn't need to. Her mother's Colombian. They speak Spanish at home.

Skills Development

1

Dear Alex,
I hope you aren't going to be cold in the tent. Are you going to have breakfast with us in the dining room tomorrow morning? Please don't cook in the tent. It's very dangerous. When do you think you are going to come back to your bedroom?
            Lots of love,
            Mom

2

Dear Mom,
Don't worry! I have my **sleeping bag** and my **comforter**. And I'm certainly not going to cook breakfast (or myself) in the tent. I have cereal and milk here for breakfast and a **thermos** of hot chocolate. I've also helped myself to a carton of orange juice from the fridge. I hope you don't mind. I have my **alarm clock**, and I'll wake myself up for school. I find it very peaceful in my tent, and of course I can listen to music all night and read if I want. I have an excellent **flashlight** and plenty of **batteries**. I have my CD player out here, and I've used Dad's **extension cord** to get electricity. So you see I've been very organized. The great thing is—nobody tells me to clean up the tent.

            Your loving son,
            Alex

3

Can I move into your tent with you? I am really sick of living with my family. Can we talk about it after this Math class?
            Luke

4 Backyard Campsite

A 14-year-old boy has moved out of his bedroom and is living in a tent in the backyard of his family home. His mother, Mrs. Flores, says, "We have not had any fights or arguments at home. We all get along very well in our family. Alex has always loved outdoor life, and he enjoys living in the backyard. But I am sure he will come back to the house soon."

5

Hi Alex,
I'm glad you are still enjoying life in your tent. Are you going to stay there forever? Can I have your old bedroom? It's bigger and brighter than mine. And Mom has made new **curtains** for the windows, and Dad has made a new shelf for your CDs. I don't understand them. Why are they doing things to your room when you live in a tent now? Anyway, is it okay for me to take your bedroom?
Your sister,
Rosa

6

Dear Rosa,
I am afraid you can't have my old bedroom. I'll call you tomorrow and explain.
            Alex

Sorry, pal. My tent is for one person only.
            Alex

Reading

1 Read the texts to find answers to these questions.

1. Where is Alex living right now? _____
2. What does he have to keep him warm at night? _____
3. Who wants to join him? _____
4. How old is Alex? _____
5. What does Rosa want to do? _____
6. What's Alex's answer to her? _____

Vocabulary

2 Guess the meanings of these words from their context. Write the correct word under each picture.

sleeping bag   comforter   thermos   alarm clock
flashlight   batteries   extension cord   ~~curtains~~

1 _curtains_   2 _____   3 _____

4 _____   5 _____   6 _____

7 _____   8 _____

Listening

3 Listen and write *T* (true) or *F* (false) next to each sentence.

1. Alex wants to come back inside. _T_
2. He can't stand up in his tent. ____
3. He has a computer in his tent. ____
4. He hasn't done any homework. ____
5. He's been back to the house ten times. ____
6. He's used the bathroom in the house. ____
7. He's used the kitchen in the middle of the night. ____
8. He doesn't want to eat cold food in the tent. ____
9. Rosa has moved into his bedroom. ____

Writing

4 Write an e-mail from Alex to a friend about his time in the tent. Use these ideas:

```
● ● ●   Send Mail: Message Composition
```

Dear _____

Last month, I moved out of my bedroom into a tent in the backyard. I decided to move because _____

Life in the tent was fun at first. I _____

But after three weeks, I was bored with the tent because _____

So I moved back to my bedroom. I really like being at home now because _____

Study Tip

Understanding the purpose of exercises

We learn better when we understand why we are doing something. Find an exercise in this unit where you …

	Page	Exercise		Page	Exercise
• practiced new vocabulary			• listened for information		
• practiced using grammar			• learned some new words		
• looked for answers in a text					

UNIT 3

Talk time

1 Complete the dialogue with the phrases.

> Don't panic   I hope   ~~It says~~
> See you   right after

Lynn What time do we have to catch the bus for the camping trip?
Chloe Hmm. Let me look at the information sheet. (1) *It says* it leaves from the school at 10:15 on Saturday morning.
Lynn But my guitar lesson only finishes at ten o'clock.
Chloe Is your lesson at home?
Lynn Yes.
Chloe Well, you can bike to the school (2) _____ _____ your guitar lesson.
Lynn (3) _____ Miss Miller isn't going to be late.
Chloe Who's Miss Miller?
Lynn She's my guitar teacher. And I don't think she has a watch! She's always late. I really don't want to miss the bus because of her.
Chloe (4) _____ . Everything's going to be okay.
Lynn You hope!
Chloe (5) _____ in front of the school at 10:15.
Lynn Bye!

2 Match the questions to the answers.

1 Why is Ben so happy today? c
2 Finally! Why are you so late?
3 What's she done wrong?
4 Where did you see Craig?
5 Cristina? Who is Cristina?
6 Why do you look so hot?

a) He was on his way to the soccer field.
b) You know, she's the girl from Mexico.
c) ~~He's won a trip to New York.~~
d) Sorry, we got on the wrong bus.
e) She's left her Math homework at home again.
f) I've run all the way from Joey's house.

26 UNIT 3

Let's Check

Vocabulary check

1 Complete the sentences with the words in the box.

> address   ambulance   envelope   international code
> cell phone   mailbox   postcards   post office   ~~stamps~~

1. Some people collect _stamps_ .
2. An e-mail _____ always has @ in it.
3. Can I borrow your _____ , please? I need to call my mother.
4. Help! There's been an accident. Call an _____ .
5. You can't put that letter in the _____ . It doesn't have a stamp on it yet.
6. People on vacation often send _____ .
7. The _____ for calling Mexico from the U.S. is 011 52.
8. When you've written a letter, you put it in an _____ .
9. You can mail letters and buy stamps at the _____ .

Grammar

2 Correct the mistake in each sentence.

> ◆ = there's a word missing
> N = change the order of two words
> X = change one word
> * = delete one word

1. Have ever they tried windsurfing? **N**
   Have they ever tried windsurfing?
2. Why she has written her name in my book? **N**
   _____
3. What you done with my stamps? ◆
   _____
4. Nice to see you—where have you been gone? *
   _____
5. You've gone to Ireland—what's it like? **X**
   _____

3 Choose the correct words for each sentence.

1. Who has ___ all the orange juice?
   A drank   B drinking   **C drunk** (circled)
2. ___ she bought a new tennis racket?
   A Was   B Did   C Has
3. The room looks great. Who ___ the table?
   A was clearing   B has cleared   C did clear
4. We've ___ to Lindsay about the tournament.
   A wrote   B write   C written
5. Has she ever ___ a race?
   A lose   B lost   C losing
6. We have ___ all the Harry Potter movies.
   A saw   B see   C seen
7. They've ___ been to Venice Beach.
   A ever   B to   C never
8. I'm bored. I ___ done anything all day.
   A haven't   B didn't   C have
9. Elly and Rob are out. They've ___ to the movies.
   A gone   B been   C went
10. Fantastic! I have ___ a trip to France.
    A win   B winning   C won
11. Why has she ___ to bed? Is she okay?
    A been   B gone   C went

4 Make sentences by putting the words in order.

1. best / Lincoln / friend / has / moved / My / to
   My best friend has moved to Lincoln.
2. eaten / has / my / Who / candy / ?
   _____
3. a / been / biking / vacation / never / on / They've
   _____
4. Abby's / gone / has / in / live / New York / sister / to
   _____
5. all / Mark / day / seen / haven't / We
   _____
6. a / been / ever / Have / in / play / school / you / ?
   _____

27
UNIT 3

UNIT 4 Movies and plays

Vocabulary

1 Match the words in the box to the posters.

ballet   comedy   concert   musical   opera   play

1 __play__   2 _____   3 _____   4 _____   5 _____   6 _____

2 Complete the crossword. The jumbled letters of the missing words are given after each clue.

Across

3 You can pick up your tickets from the ___ at six o'clock. (XBO EFFICO)
5 I had a fantastic ___ . I was at the front of the theater. (TASE)
7 Learn your ___ before the dress rehearsal. (ESNIL)
8 My ___ was amazing. I wore a big green hat and silver pants. (MESTUOC)
9 In the last ___ there was a real horse on the stage. (ENECS)
12 Ladies and gentlemen, tonight's ___ of *Cinderella* will begin in three minutes. (CAPERFERMON)
13 ___ act in plays. (ROCTAS)
14 The actors in a theater perform on a ___ (GESTA)

Down

1 Did you have a big ___ in the play? (TRAP)
2 The ___ of the play was very simple, but it wasn't boring. (LOPT)
4 A big group of classical musicians. (ACHESTORR)
6 The ___ loved the opera. They clapped and shouted. (DANCEUIE)
10 You can read about the actors in the ___ . (MGARROP)
11 We all wrote the ___ of our school play. (TRICPS)

Dialogue work

3 Complete the dialogue with the correct sentences.

Mom	You're late. Where have you been?
Maddie	We had an extra rehearsal. (1) _____ .
Mom	Has he learned his lines yet?
Maddie	Yes, he has. (2) _____ .
Mom	When are you going to do the programs?
Maddie	(3) _____ .
	I got up at six o'clock this morning, and I did them on your computer.
Mom	You must be tired and hungry.
Maddie	I am. (4) _____ . Is dinner ready?
Mom	Yes. (5) _____ . Help yourself.
Maddie	Yummy! (6) _____ .
Mom	Yes. I ate at six o'clock when I got home.

- And his mom has made him a great costume.
- Have you already eaten?
- I haven't eaten anything since breakfast.
- I've already done them.
- I've made lasagna with spinach and cheese.
- Then I went back to Adam's.

Study Tip

Practicing the present perfect

You need to know past participles to make the present perfect. The best way to learn them is to use them. At the end of the school day, ask a friend to tell you three things he/she has done during the day.

What have you done today?

I've had a Math test. I've played volleyball. I've sent ten text messages to my friends.

Grammar practice

4 Use the phrases to write captions with *just* and the present perfect.

- go to the salon
- have dinner
- lose the game
- ~~finish her book~~
- see a ghost
- speak to Katie
- win $1,000

1 <u>She's just finished her book.</u>

2 _____

3 _____

4 _____

5 _____

6 _____

7 "Would you like something to eat?" "No, thanks. _____ ."

There is a list of irregular past participles on page 137 of the Student's Book.

UNIT 4

5 Use the prompts to write responses in the present perfect with *already*.

1. A: I should empty the trash can.
   B: It's okay. I / empty / it
   It's okay. I've already emptied it.

2. A: We should send an invitation to Linda.
   B: Dave / send / her / one
   _____

3. A: I have to do my Science project this weekend.
   B: Poor you! I / do / mine
   _____

4. A: I want to go swimming.
   B: We / go
   _____

5. A: What do you want for lunch?
   B: Nothing, thanks. We / eat
   _____

6. A: Does Bethany want to come to the school play?
   B: No, she / see it.
   _____

7. A: Let's go out when it stops raining.
   B: It / stop.
   _____

6 Use the prompts to write questions with the present perfect + *yet* and answers with *going to*.

1. A: you / write to Serena ?
   Have you written to Serena yet?
   B: write / tomorrow
   No, I'm going to write to her tomorrow.

2. A: Mark / tell his parents?
   _____
   B: not tell
   _____

3. A: Claire / buy a hamster?
   _____
   B: buy one / on Saturday
   _____

4. A: you / speak to Gary?
   _____
   B: speak / later
   _____

5. A: Laura / make the cake?
   _____
   B: make / tomorrow
   _____

6. A: you / take a picture of us?
   _____
   B: take one / in a minute
   _____

7 Look at the checklist for the school play. Write what people have already done and what they haven't done yet.

SCHOOL PLAY

1. Tanya and Kate: finish Ryan's costume (✗)
2. Isobel: take the pictures for the programs (✔)
3. Sam: write the programs (✔)
4. Tanya: find a necklace for Kristen (✗)
5. Isobel: check the lights on the stage (✗)
6. Mark and Dan: move the piano (✔)

1. *Tanya and Kate haven't finished Ryan's costume yet.*
2. *Isobel has already taken the pictures for the programs.*
3. _____
4. _____
5. _____
6. _____

8 Use the words and phrases below to write questions with *How long...?* in the present perfect and answers with *for* or *since*.

1 **A:** you / know Jen?
   How long have you known Jen?
   B: three years
   I've known her for three years.

2 **A:** your grandmother / have that motorcycle?
   How long has your grandmother had that motorcycle?
   B: 1999
   She's had it since 1999.

3 **A:** Sara / be in the shower?
   _____
   B: an hour
   _____

4 **A:** they / live in Arizona?
   _____
   B: three or four years
   _____

5 **A:** Alex / work at the gym?
   _____
   B: July
   _____

6 **A:** you / wear glasses?
   _____
   B: I was ten
   _____

7 **A:** Amy / have your CDs?
   _____
   B: two weeks
   _____

8 **A:** they / be in Minneapolis?
   _____
   B: three days
   _____

9 Check (✔) the four other correct sentences. Make an ✘ next to the five other incorrect sentences and write them correctly.

a) I've just seen a really scary movie. ✔
b) Mom wants to go to the new Chinese restaurant. We never been there ✘
c) Belinda didn't speak to me since the party. ☐
d) Has Carol moved to her new house yet? ☐
e) I gave her some earrings last week, and she already loses them. ☐
f) I'm tired. I've just been to the gym. ☐
g) I've lost my keys. I can't find them anywhere. ☐
h) Sam and Rob have come back from Portland yesterday. ☐
i) We've been to the beach last weekend. ☐
j) What time have you gone to bed last night? ☐
k) Your hair looks nice. What have you done to it? ☐

1 We've never been there.
2 _____
3 _____
4 _____
5 _____
6 _____

10 Write five sentences about you, your friends, or your family using the present perfect and *for* or *since*.

Josie has been at this school for two years.
We have had a dog since 1999.

1 _____ had _____
2 _____ been in/at _____
3 _____ known _____
4 _____ lived _____
5 _____ studied _____

CULTURE SPOT

Junior High School

Hi Zoe,

Thanks for your e-mail. Your school sounds **awesome**. I would really like to go to an English boarding school like yours. My school is totally ordinary. So why do you want to know about it?!! Anyway, here goes …

I'm in the 8th **grade** at Alice Deal Junior High, Washington, D.C. In the U.S., kids start in first grade at age six and finish in twelfth grade. For seventh through ninth grade, you go to junior high school. In some places, you go to middle school for sixth through eighth grade.

At some schools, the kids have to wear uniforms. We don't have a uniform, but there is a dress code. That means kids shouldn't go to school in baggy skateboarding **pants**, or really short skirts, or clothes with holes in them. And kids can't dye their hair crazy colors!

School starts at 8:45 and ends at 3:15. A lot of kids stay until 5:30 to play sports or go to the after-school program. That means you can stay at school to do your **assignments** or go to the computer lab. Last year, my Math **grades** were really bad, so I did Math in the after-school program. Now my Math is okay, but I still don't like it. My favorite subject is **Phys Ed**.

We do the same subjects as you, but we do Spanish instead of French. That's because there are a lot of people in the U.S. who speak Spanish at home. Some schools in Washington, D.C. are totally bilingual in Spanish and English because there are so many Latino kids. Their parents or grandparents are from Central America originally, mainly from El Salvador.

We have lunch in the **cafeteria** at school. The food is okay. Today we had pizza for lunch. We also have a fifteen-minute **recess** in the morning.

One of the best things at my school is the **field trips**. Last week, we went on a biology field trip to Kenilworth Aquatic Gardens. It's a national park with a river and lakes. We spent the morning there and ate lunch in the picnic area. There are hundreds of water birds, and we also saw turtles, frogs, and water snakes. The plants are kind of tropical. There are pink and white flowers in all the lakes. It is totally cool.

Only one week now until the summer **vacation**. Then I'll be free for over ten weeks. I'm going to sailing camp for three weeks with my friend Doug. I can't wait.

Hope you like these photos. Write back!

Danny

Reading

1 Read the letter and find short answers to these questions.

1 Which country is Zoe's school in? _____
2 Which country does Danny live in? _____
3 Does he wear a school uniform? _____
4 Which subject doesn't he like? _____
5 Which language does he study? _____
6 Name three things to see at Kenilworth Aquatic Gardens. _____

2 Match each caption to a photo.

a) This is a basketball game at my school.
b) The plants at Kenilworth were awesome.
c) This is me in the school cafeteria. Burgers and french fries is my favorite school lunch.
d) It was hard to get this picture. The frog didn't want to sit still!

Vocabulary

3 Match the American English words to the British English words.

American English		British English
1 awesome	b	a) holiday
2 eighth grade	☐	b) amazing
3 pants	☐	c) marks
4 assignments	☐	d) year eight
5 grades	☐	e) class visit
6 Phys Ed	☐	f) PE
7 cafeteria	☐	g) canteen
8 recess	☐	h) break
9 field trip	☐	i) trousers
10 vacation	☐	j) homework

4 Guess the meaning of these words and write a translation in your language. Then check in a dictionary.

1 turtles _____
2 frogs _____

Project

5 Write about you and your school.

What's the name of your school?
_____
_____

How long have you been there?
_____

What kind of school is it?
_____

Do you wear a uniform?
_____

Is there a dress code? What can/can't you wear?
_____
_____

What time does your school day start and end?
_____
_____

What grade are you in?
_____

What subjects do you study?
_____
_____

How many students are there in your class?
_____

What kind of exams do you have at your school?
_____
_____

Do you go to any classes after school? What are they?
_____
_____

What's the best thing about your school?
_____
_____

What's the worst thing about your school?
_____
_____

UNIT 4

Listening

1 Listen to the radio advertisement and complete the form.

This is your chance to do something about (1) _litter_ on your local beach.

National Beach day is on (2) _____

It starts at (3) _____ .

We'll clean up the beach by collecting candy wrappers, (4) _____ and

(5) _____ .

There will be lots of fun activities, such as games and races, (6) _____ and

(7) _____ .

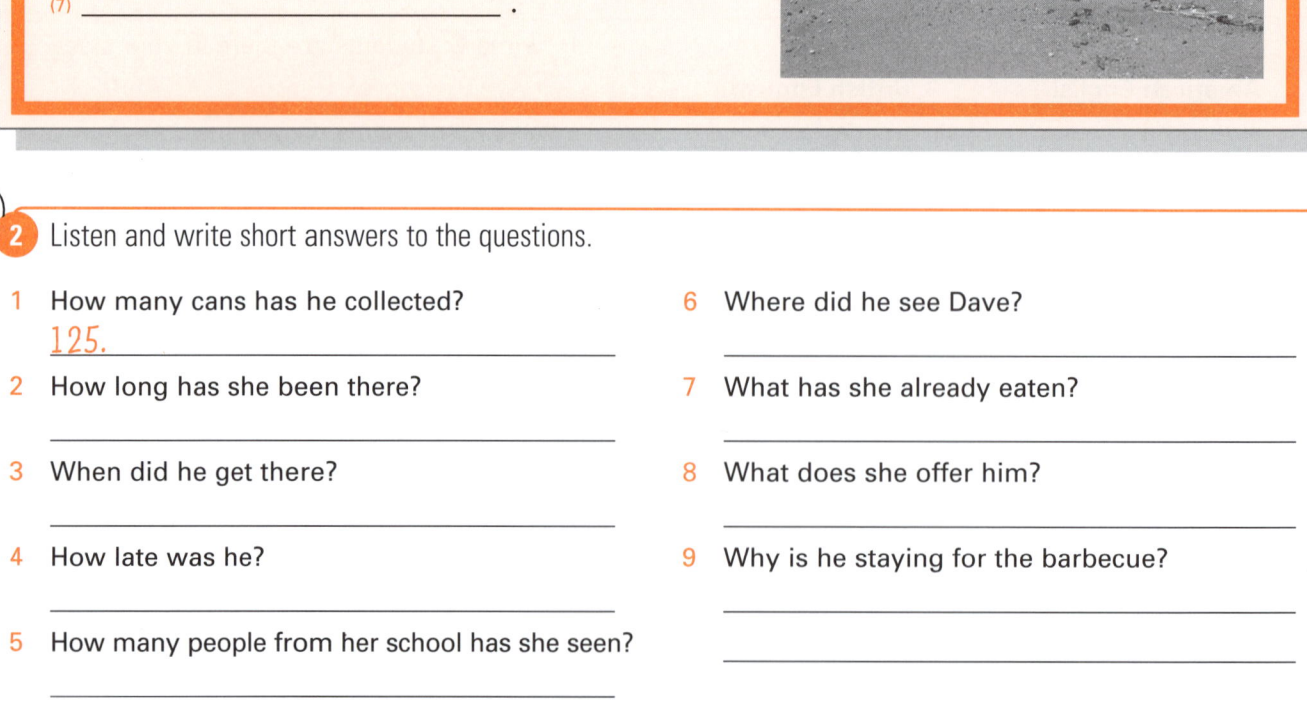

2 Listen and write short answers to the questions.

1 How many cans has he collected?
   125.

2 How long has she been there?
   _____

3 When did he get there?
   _____

4 How late was he?
   _____

5 How many people from her school has she seen?
   _____

6 Where did he see Dave?
   _____

7 What has she already eaten?
   _____

8 What does she offer him?
   _____

9 Why is he staying for the barbecue?
   _____

Let's Check

Vocabulary check

1 What are they talking about? Match the types of shows to what people said about them.

> play   comedy   ballet   ~~musical~~   concert   opera

1. I love *Cats*. There are so many great songs. _musical_
2. They were all fantastic dancers. _____
3. I love Verdi. *Aida* is his best. _____
4. I haven't laughed like that for months! _____
5. I liked the piano solo best. _____
6. It was a difficult plot, but I enjoyed it. _____

2 Choose the correct words for the blanks.

> audience   costumes   lines   main character   orchestra
> performances   plot   program   scene   ~~seats~~   stage

1. "Where are our _seats_?" "We're B6 and B7, near the front."
2. "Who played Juliet?" "I don't know. Check in the _____."
3. Get the _____ ready for the dress rehearsal on Friday.
4. We're doing three _____ of *Cinderella*—one on Friday and two on Saturday.
5. The play went well. Nobody forgot their _____.
6. He's a fantastic actor. He always plays the _____ in school plays.
7. The _____ loved the comedy. They laughed at all the jokes.
8. Billy plays the trumpet in the school _____.
9. In opera, the story or _____ isn't very important. The music and singing are the most important things.
10. At the end of the play, we went on to the _____ and danced with the actors.
11. I liked the party _____ best. The costumes were great.

Grammar check

3 Correct the mistake in each sentence.

> ◆ = there's a word missing   N = change the order of two words
> X = change one word   * = delete one word

1. They just have left. **N**
   They have just left.
2. We've known him since three years. **X**
   _____
3. I already have finished my lunch. **N**
   _____
4. Charlie has not went to school yet. **X**
   _____
5. She's been here nine o'clock. ◆
   _____
6. It's eight o'clock and he's already been gone to bed. *
   _____

4 Choose the correct words for each sentence.

1. ___ found his glasses yet?
   A He has   **B** Did he   **(C)** Has he
2. Maria has worked there ___ October.
   A for   **B** since   **C** just
3. My sister ___ bought a new scooter.
   A just has   **B** has just   **C** did
4. We have had a dog ___ a year.
   A for   **B** since   **C** after
5. Louise ___ at this school since 2003.
   A has gone   **B** was   **C** has been
6. I've ___ seen that movie.
   A already   **B** yet   **C** have
7. I haven't made the cake ___.
   A already   **B** yet   **C** just
8. I ___ George for years.
   A didn't see   **B** seen   **C** haven't seen
9. He has ___ gone out.
   A for   **B** last   **C** just
10. How long ___ lived there?
    A he   **B** has he   **C** they
11. I ___ written to her twice this month.
    A already   **B** have already   **C** have just

UNIT 4

UNIT 4 Practice

Vocabulary

1 Who are these signs for? Circle A, B, or C.

1. **Baggage reclaim**
   - A people at a gym
   - B schoolchildren
   - C tourists ⟵ (circled)

2. **Programs $5**
   - A actors
   - B the audience at a play
   - C volunteers at an animal shelter

3. **Italy .... 1 / USA 1**
   - A the audience at a play
   - B people at a game
   - C teachers

4. **Don't forget the zip code!**
   - A students
   - B people in a library
   - C customers in a post office

5. **Have you washed your hands?**
   - A workers in a kitchen
   - B actors
   - C soccer players

6. **Please take your seats.**
   - A tourists
   - B teachers
   - C the audience at a play

2 Match the descriptions to the correct travel word.

1. You buy these to travel on a bus, train, or plane. — **h**
2. You go here to catch a plane. — ☐
3. It travels across the ocean. — ☐
4. Only one or two people can travel on it. — ☐
5. It carries things in the back of it and travels between towns. — ☐
6. It can be a suitcase, a backpack, or a bag. — ☐

a) airport
b) bus stop
c) truck
d) departure
e) ferry
f) luggage
g) scooter
h) ~~tickets~~

Dialogue work

3 Complete the conversation between the customer and the shop assistant.

Shop assistant Hello. Can I help you?
Customer (1) _f_
Shop assistant How long ago did you buy it?
Customer (2) _____
Shop assistant And what exactly is the problem?
Customer (3) _____
Shop assistant I'm sorry about that. I can give you another one, or you can have your money back.
Customer (4) _____
Shop assistant All right. Could you sign this form first, please?
Customer (5) _____
Shop assistant Thank you. Here's a new clock for you.
Customer (6) _____
Shop assistant I'm sure you won't have a problem this time. They're normally very good clocks.

a) I never use a clock.
b) I'd like to exchange it for another one, please.
c) The alarm doesn't work. I was late for class this morning because it didn't wake me up.
d) It was fairly expensive. It cost $30.
e) Just last week. It's still in its box.
f) ~~Yes, please. I bought this alarm clock here and it doesn't work now.~~
g) Thanks. Are you sure this one is going to work?
h) Yes, of course.

Writing

4 You have to go out. Write a note to your friend Zoe, who is staying with you.

Say:
- where you are going and why
- when you will be back

Write 20–25 words.

_____
_____
_____
_____
_____

Listening

5 Listen to five short conversations. Check (✔) the right answer.

1 What does she buy?

A ☐ B ☐ C ✔

2 When's the next train to Kingston?

A ☐ B ☐ C ☐

3 How much is the tennis racket?

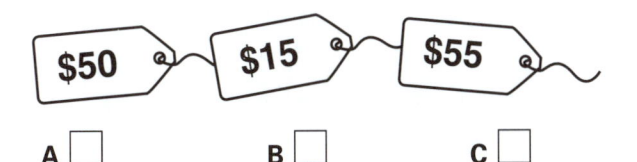

$50 $15 $55

A ☐ B ☐ C ☐

4 When is the dress rehearsal?

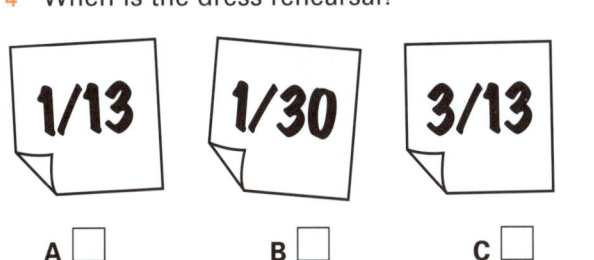

1/13 1/30 3/13

A ☐ B ☐ C ☐

5 What does she need?

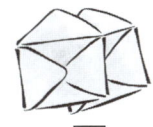

A ☐ B ☐ C ☐

6 Listen to Emma and Josh talking about activity vacations. What activity can you do in each country? Write a letter a–h next to each country.

COUNTRIES		ACTIVITIES
1 France	b	a) horseback riding
2 Spain	☐	b) visiting castles
3 Portugal	☐	c) tennis
4 Italy	☐	d) windsurfing
5 Scotland	☐	e) dancing
6 Ireland	☐	f) water-skiing
		g) camping
		h) art galleries and museums

7 You will hear some information about boat trips. Listen and complete the bulletin board.

River Rides Summer Boat Trips—Ocoee River

Summer season starts: (1) _May 1_
Summer season ends: (2) _____
Trips leave from: (3) _____
First trip leaves at: (4) _____
Last trip leaves at: (5) _____
Trips take: (6) _____
Price   (adults) (7) _____
             (children) (8) _____
To book, call: (9) 888- _____
Our office is at: (10) _____ River Street, Chattanooga

UNIT 5
Farms and farm animals

Vocabulary

1 Find ten more animals in the word square. The words go in these directions: ➡, ↗, ↘

B	S	H	E	E	P	W	L
F	P	D	B	U	L	L	T
P	O	W	U	E	C	A	B
A	O	X	S	C	O	A	N
C	J	R	W	G	K	E	T
G	O	O	S	E	H	J	J
H	E	D	O	G	U	R	M

2 Match the words to the numbers.

barn   _3_
farmhouse __
fence __
field __
gate __
pond __
stable __
tree __
yard __

Dialogue work

3 Complete the dialogue with the correct words.

> across banana bull course cow farmer
> ~~field~~ gates his know problem

Jon Come on. Let's go across this (1) _field_ .
Maddie The (2) _____ will be really angry if he sees us.
Jon No, he won't.
Maddie How do you (3) _____ ?
Jon Because my dad's the farmer, and it's (4) _____ field.
Maddie Oh.
Jon Anyway, farmers only get angry if people leave the (5) _____ open. Come on.
Maddie I still don't want to go (6) _____ that field.
Jon What's the (7) _____ now?
Maddie I'm scared of that (8) _____ .
Jon That's a (9) _____ , silly.
Maddie Are you sure?
Jon Of (10) _____ I'm sure. Now, come on.
Maddie If it is a bull, what will we do?
Jon Listen, Maddie, if that's a bull, I'm a (11) _____ .

Grammar practice

4 Put the words in order to make sentences. Add a comma (,) where necessary.

1 don't / miss / hurry / the / If / we'll / train / we
   If we don't hurry, we'll miss the train.

2 all the / annoyed / be / cake / eat / if / Josie / we / will
   _____
   _____

3 do / can't find / farm / if / the / What / we / we / will / ?
   _____
   _____

4 *Ghost Night* / movies / If / like / love / scary / you / you'll
   _____
   _____

5 a / doesn't / have / If / it / picnic / rain / tomorrow / we'll
   _____
   _____

6 be / can / come / if / It / nice / on / really / Saturday / will / you
   _____
   _____

5 Match the sentence halves and write the full sentences. Add a comma (,) where necessary.

1 If it rains   [g]
2 Do bulls really get angry   [ ]
3 What do you do   [ ]
4 My mother gets worried   [ ]
5 If I drink coffee at night   [ ]
6 If my sister borrows my things   [ ]
7 In basketball, you can't run   [ ]

a) I can't sleep.
b) if I come home late.
c) if you can't sleep?
d) if you have the ball.
e) if you wear something red?
f) she always loses them.
g) ~~we have PE inside.~~

1 _If it rains, we have PE inside._
2 _____
3 _____
4 _____
5 _____
6 _____
7 _____

UNIT 5

6 Write sentences using *if* + present simple in the first clause, and *might/might not* + verb in the second clause.

1 you (sit) on that table / it (break)
   If you sit on that table, it might break.

2 you (go) to the park now / you (find) Lily
   _____

3 the weather (be) nice tomorrow / we (have) a barbecue
   _____

4 I (have) enough money by July / I (buy) a new camera
   _____

5 Kate (not do) some work / she (not pass) her exams
   _____

6 you (not shut) the gate / the sheep (get) out
   _____

7 I (not go) to soccer today / Josh (not let) me be in the next game
   _____

8 we (sit) in the backyard / I (not hear) the phone
   _____

9 you (not write) this down / you (not remember) it
   _____

> Don't confuse *has* as a main verb and *has* as an auxiliary verb:
> She **has** a car, **doesn't she**?
> She **has** bought it, **hasn't she**?

7 Write sentences in the first conditional using the verbs in (brackets).

1 We '*ll be* late if we *don't go* now. (be / not go)
2 If you _____ another cup of coffee, you _____ tonight. (have / not sleep)
3 If you _____ to bed now, you _____ tired in the morning (not go / be)
4 There _____ any breakfast if Jon _____ the eggs. (not be / not gather)
5 If our cat _____ kittens, we _____ one to you. (have / give)
6 I _____ upset if Jamie _____ my birthday again. (be / forget)
7 If we _____ across the field, it _____ quicker. (walk / be)
8 I _____ you if you _____ a party tomorrow. (help / have)
9 If Naomi _____ soon, we _____ without her. (not arrive / go)

8 Complete the questions with the correct tags.

1 You live in Cambridge, *don't you* ?
2 Anna made this cake, _____ ?
3 Ben's at your school, _____ ?
4 It'll be cold later, _____ ?
5 It's hot, _____ ?
6 Lucy was angry, _____ ?
7 She has blond hair, _____ ?
8 You're Mexican, _____ ?
9 Steve speaks Spanish, _____ ?
10 The hens were hungry, _____ ?
11 They've lived here for ages, _____ ?
12 We can go across this field, _____ ?
13 You have a rabbit, _____ ?
14 There was a terrible storm, _____ ?
15 Your dad has been to China, _____ ?

9 Complete the questions with the correct tags.

1. You don't eat meat, _do you_ ?
2. Adam doesn't have a brother, _____ ?
3. You won't tell Mom, _____ ?
4. I wasn't going very fast, _____ ?
5. Maria hasn't written, _____ ?
6. You can't ride a horse, _____ ?
7. Paul doesn't like fish, _____ ?
8. You weren't listening, _____ ?
9. The party wasn't very good, _____ ?
10. There weren't many people there, _____ ?
11. They didn't enjoy the play, _____ ?
12. You don't have a scooter, _____ ?
13. This isn't your puppy, _____ ?
14. Your parents haven't left yet, _____ ?

10 Match the sentence halves. Write the sentences, adding question tags.

1. [e] Penguins can't _fly, can they?_
2. [ ] Frankfurt isn't _____
3. [ ] Marilyn Monroe was _____
4. [ ] Picasso painted _____
5. [ ] Spiders have _____
6. [ ] A lot of coffee comes _____
7. [ ] There aren't any _____
8. [ ] *Volleyball* has _____
9. [ ] *Juan* is _____
10. [ ] Most cats don't _____

a) a Spanish name
b) a movie star
c) from Brazil
d) eight legs
e) ~~fly~~
f) four Ls in it
g) swim
h) the capital of Germany
i) *Guernica*
j) tigers in Africa

11 Make polite requests for each picture using one of these phrases:

- Do you mind if
- Is it all right if
- May I

1. _Is it all right if I use your phone?_
2. _____
3. _____
4. _____
5. _____
6. _____

Skills Development

Blind people might soon start using ponies instead of dogs as guides. In the U.S., Cuddles, the world's first guide pony, started working in May this year. She has already gotten on and off planes with her owner, Dan Shaw, and gone up and down escalators at airports. Cuddles, a miniature pony, is only 52 centimeters high and is very calm. She is not scared of traffic and doesn't panic on busy streets. Dan Shaw, who has been blind for 27 years, says, "Cuddles is part of my family now." Janet Burleson, Cuddles's trainer, is also very pleased with Cuddles. She says, "You can train a horse to do anything a dog can do. Cuddles understands 23 commands, including 'wait' and 'forward.' And she is very clean. If she needs to go outside, she stamps her foot!"

There are a lot of good reasons to use miniature horses as guides for the blind. Horses have an instinct to guide. If a wild horse goes blind, another horse will often look after it. And if a rider hurts himself, his horse will often carry him safely home. Miniature ponies live 30 to 40 years. Guide dogs can only work for about twelve years. It's also cheaper to train a guide pony. It costs $55,000 to train a guide dog and only $15,000 to train a guide pony. Horses have excellent memories. They don't forget dangerous situations, and they always look for the safest routes. Horses are healthy and strong and don't get tired if they have to travel a long way. They also have excellent eyes and can see in the dark. Horses do not try to get attention from humans all the time like dogs.

Some people say horses are more nervous than dogs. "If a horse gets scared, it wants to run away," says Patrick Mactaggart, a professional dog trainer. "I think dogs will always be the best guides for the blind." But Dan Shaw doesn't agree. "I've always loved horses," he says. "I never expected to own one. And I never expected it to be my eyes."

Reading

1 Read the text and choose the best title for it.

1 Guide Dogs Are Best
2 **A Very Expensive Animal**
3 Ponies Help the Blind
4 **Blind for 27 Years**
5 A Very Clever Dog
6 **A Dangerous Job**

2 Write *T* (true) or *F* (false).

1 Cuddles has been on a plane. ___
2 Cuddles is a large horse. ___
3 Cuddles is scared of cars. ___
4 Horses often help their riders. ___
5 Ponies only live about twelve years. ___
6 Ponies are more expensive to train than dogs. ___
7 Horses remember a lot. ___
8 Horses can see in the dark. ___

Writing

3 Imagine you saw Dan Shaw and Cuddles in your town. Write a letter to a friend about them in your notebook. Use information in the article and your imagination. Use these notes to help you.

Dear _____ ,
Last week I was (*in/at*) _____
when I saw a blind man with a guide pony.
I was really surprised. The pony was (*describe the pony*) _____ .
It helped the man to _____ .
When the man wanted to _____ ,
the pony _____ .
The pony could _____ .
I've seen a guide dog, but I've never seen a guide pony. What about you?
Love,
_____

Study Tip

4 When you read or listen in your own language, you can often guess the endings of the sentence. Try to guess the endings of these sentences. Then listen and compare your answers.

1 I fell out of the boat into the pond and lost my _____
2 I didn't go to the gym because I couldn't find _____
3 The workers took the bananas off the boat and put them in _____
4 She chose the gray kitten because it was _____
5 He wanted to be a vet because he _____
6 He wrote a long letter to her, but he didn't mail it because _____

Listening

5 Maddie is talking about horseback riding. Guess how these sentences end. Write your guesses in pencil. Then listen and check your answers.

1 I love horses, and I'm pretty good at _____
2 Unfortunately, I don't have my own _____
3 And of course, riding is very _____
4 I don't get enough allowance to pay for _____
5 Last year, I got a weekend job in a _____
6 I go there every Saturday afternoon for about _____
7 I brush the _____
8 I also give them _____
9 The longest job is cleaning the _____
10 The owners don't _____
11 But I get a free ride at the _____
12 I'm very _____

UNIT 5

Talk Time

1 Write the phrases in the correct balloons.

- Don't worry.
- for ages
- I wish I could go.
- Just one thing
- much later
- ~~That's okay.~~

I've forgotten my swimming goggles.
(1) *That's okay.* I have two pairs.

They're going fishing again.
(2) _____

I haven't been skating (3) _____

Hurry! The train leaves in ten minutes.
(4) _____ We'll be there on time.

I got up at eleven this morning. How about you?

I got up (5) _____ It was around two in the afternoon.

(6) _____ : have you passed your driving test?

2 Complete the dialogues with these words:

> all   course   fine   Go   ~~May~~
> mind   right   Would

A: (1) _May_ I use your phone?
B: Yes, of (2) _____ .

A: (3) _____ you like a drink?
B: No, thank you.

A: Do you (4) _____ if I close the window?
B: Not at (5) _____ . (6) _____ ahead.

A: I'll call you tomorrow, if that's all (7) _____ .
B: Yes, that'll be (8) _____ .

44
UNIT 5

Let's Check

Vocabulary check

1 Put the letters in order to make animal words.

1. act — cat
2. lubl — _____
3. woc — _____
4. shore — _____
5. knodey — _____
6. heeps — _____
7. toga — _____
8. cukd — _____
9. sogoe — _____
10. tenkit — _____
11. yuppp — _____

2 Match the animals to the places where they are kept.

1. hens — e
2. sheep — ☐
3. cows — ☐
4. ducks — ☐
5. horses — ☐

a) stable
b) field
c) pond
d) barn
e) ~~yard~~

Grammar check

3 Correct the mistake in each sentence.

- ◆ = there's a word missing
- N = change the order of two words
- X = change one word
- * = delete one word

1. You went to a party last week, hadn't you? **X**
   You went to a party last week, didn't you?
2. If you run, you might to find her at the bus stop. *****
   _____
3. Do you mind I borrow your dictionary for a minute? ◆
   _____
4. If you will write to her, please give her my love. *****
   _____
5. I may have another glass of water? **N**
   _____
6. We always read on the bus, don't she? **X**
   _____

4 Choose the correct words for each sentence.

1. She hasn't eaten all the potato chips, ____ ?
   A was she (**B has she**) C did she
2. If I ____ him, I'll tell you.
   A see B will see C saw
3. If you give me her address, I might ____ to her.
   A to write B write C writing
4. She has dark hair, ____ ?
   A doesn't she B isn't it C isn't she
5. Do you mind ____ I turn the light on?
   A if B that C for
6. If Jodie is late again, ____ wait for her.
   A I won't B I wasn't C I'll be
7. The kittens didn't want their food, ____ ?
   A were they B did they C didn't they
8. You've shut the gate, ____ ?
   A haven't you B didn't you C hasn't it
9. You won't tell anyone, ____ you?
   A do B can C will
10. You haven't been to Puerto Rico, ____ you?
    A did B have C were
11. If you know her name, please ____ me.
    A telling B told C tell

5 Make sentences by putting the words in order.

1. I / if / Do / mind / open / the / window / you / ?
   Do you mind if I open the window?
2. bus / won't leave / The / us, / will it / without / ?
   _____
3. to gather / do it / the eggs, / have time / If you don't / I'll
   _____
4. can I have / the car, / extra / If I / allowance / some / wash / ?
   _____
5. burn / fire / if you / might / too near / sit / the / You / yourself
   _____

UNIT 5

UNIT 6 Jobs

Vocabulary

1 What are the jobs? Put the letters in the right order. Then match the jobs to the pictures.

1. CHARITTEC — architect — c
2. FECH — ____
3. STINTED — _____
4. MARREF — _____
5. HARIREDSERS — h___ d_____
6. ROJUNSTILA — j_____
7. FILEDRAUG — l___g_____
8. SURNE — _____
9. POORHATPHERG — p_____
10. CORK CUSMIANI — r___ m_____
11. TISTNICES — s_____
12. OZO PERKEE — z__ k_____

a. camera
b. tractor
c. drawing desk
d. guitar
e. lab equipment
f. chef's hat and utensils
g. elephant in cage
h. dentist tools
i. lifeguard pool
j. hairdryer and scissors
k. nurse's hat and thermometer
l. notepad and microphone

Dialogue work

2 Complete the dialogue with the correct words.

> grandmother   lovely   ~~arm~~   poor   scared
> money   joking   try   mind

Maddie Watch out. There's a really big spider on your (1) _arm_ .

Rachel Where? I can't see one.

Maddie Just (2) _____ ! I said it to scare you.

Rachel Well, you didn't scare me.

Maddie Too bad! You used to be (3) _____ of spiders.

Rachel I used to be, but I don't (4) _____ them now.

Maddie My (5) _____ says spiders are lucky.

Rachel Lucky?

Maddie She says if a spider walks across your hand, you get (6) _____ .

Rachel Really?

Maddie Yes. You should (7) _____ it some time.

Rachel I don't mind looking at them, but I still hate having them on me.

Maddie But think of all that (8) _____ money!

Rachel It's okay, thanks. I prefer being (9) _____ .

Grammar practice

3 When the Gardner family moved from Chicago to a small town on the beach, their son Nick's life changed a lot.

a) **Before:**
1. he lived in an apartment on a busy street.
2. he took the bus to school.
3. he studied German.
4. he played soccer on Wednesdays.
5. he wore a school uniform.
6. he spent all his free time skateboarding.

b) **Now:**
1. he lives in a big house with a yard.
2. he bikes to school.
3. he studies Spanish.
4. he does track and field on Wednesdays.
5. he wears jeans to school.
6. he spends all his free time surfing.

a) **Write sentences with *He used to ...* .**
1. He used to live in an apartment on a busy street.
2. _____
3. _____
4. _____
5. _____
6. _____

b) **Write sentences with *He didn't use to...* .**
1. He didn't use to live in a big house with a yard.
2. _____
3. _____
4. _____
5. _____
6. _____

4 Write sentences with *used to/didn't use to* and the present or past simple.

1. I (not like) *didn't use to like* coffee, but now I (drink) *drink* it every day.
2. Amy (not have) *didn't use to have* a dog, but she (get) *got* one last year.
3. Mark (have) _____ a scooter, but he (sell) _____ it last week.
4. Lee Ann (not do) _____ sports, but now she (play) _____ tennis every week.
5. Jamie (live) _____ in New York, but he (move) _____ to Erie two years ago.
6. We (not like) _____ each other, but we (be) _____ friends now.
7. People (write) _____ a lot of letters, but now they (send) _____ e-mails.
8. You (fight) _____ with your brother, but now you (fight) _____ with your sister.

Study Tip

Chain games

To practice new vocabulary, you can make up chain games and play them in small or large groups. Here's one for you to try:

A: In my street, there's a doctor.
B: In my street, there's a doctor and a chef.
C: In my street, there's a doctor, a chef, and a rock musician.

Each person adds an item to the list. If someone gets the chain wrong, you have to start again.

5 Read the text, then write the interviewer's questions using a verb from the box with *use to* or the present simple.

> buy   get   go   live   ~~work~~

THE MILLIONAIRE STUDENT
Two years ago, 25-year-old Felicia Donovan was a sales assistant in a shoe shop. Then she won $10 million, and her life changed completely. Felicia told us, "I'm still the same person, but I don't have to worry about money now."

1 <u>Where did you use to work</u>?
In a shoe shop.
2 <u>Where do you work now</u>?
I don't work. I'm at college again. I'm studying.
3 _____?
I shared a very small dark apartment with two other girls.
4 _____?
I have a beautiful house with a pool in upstate New York.
5 _____ to work?
I used to bike.
6 _____ to your classes in college now?
I drive there in my Porsche.
7 _____ for your vacations?
I used to go camping in the Adirondack Mountains.
8 _____ for your vacations now?
To the Caribbean, Thailand, the Seychelles.
9 _____ your clothes?
I didn't buy any new clothes. My cousins gave me their old clothes.
10 _____ your clothes now?
Gucci, Valentino, Versace! Money isn't a problem!

6 Complete the captions with the correct phrases.

- cross this road
- go downhill
- learn a new language
- ~~run across roads~~
- sleep all day
- put your head in the sand
- swim in the rain

1 <u>It's</u> dangerous <u>to</u> <u>run across roads.</u>

2 _____ difficult _____
_____
_____

3 _____ easy _____
_____
_____

4 _____ fun _____
_____
_____

5 _____ boring _____
_____
_____

6 _____ silly _____
_____
_____

7 _____ impossible _____
_____
_____

7 Write eight sentences giving your opinion about the activities.

> boring   dangerous   difficult   embarrassing
> fun   great   ~~important~~   impossible   silly

1 _It's important to_ do sports every week.
2 _____ be good at music.
3 _____ stay in bed all day.
4 _____ surf the Internet.
5 _____ learn about different countries.
6 _____ climb trees.
7 _____ forget your lines in a play.
8 _____ fight with people.

8 Complete the sentences, putting the verbs into the correct form.

1 I don't like _living_ (live) here. I'd prefer _to live_ (live) by the ocean.
2 She doesn't enjoy _____ (be) the center of attention.
3 Would you like _____ (get) a job as a TV announcer?
4 She plans _____ (spend) the summer working on a farm.
5 Andy's learning _____ (surf) this summer.
6 I don't mind _____ (stay) in this evening.
7 I didn't expect _____ (see) you here.
8 I prefer _____ (swim) to _____ (lie) in the sun.
9 We should try _____ (meet) before the weekend.
10 I really hate _____ (get) up early.
11 You don't need _____ (bring) any food to the picnic.
12 Do you enjoy _____ (go) for walks by the river?
13 Melissa wants _____ (get) tickets for the concert.
14 I love _____ (wear) these shoes. They're so comfortable.
15 I hope _____ (get) a job in the movies one day.
16 Why have you given up _____ (go) to dance classes?
17 He can't help _____ (be) so boring!

9 Match the sentence halves and write the complete sentences using an infinitive of purpose.

1 We're staying at home _to watch the big game._ [f]
2 I'm going to the post office _____ ☐
3 He's gone to the café _____ ☐
4 Are you using the computer _____ ? ☐
5 I've bought some tomatoes _____ ☐
6 Do you want to come to the park _____ ? ☐
7 Did you call Maria _____ ☐

a) ask about the rehearsal
b) buy some stamps
c) have coffee with Simon
d) make a pasta sauce
e) play baseball
f) ~~watch the big game~~
g) write your Science project

CULTURE SPOT

Mackinac Island *by Hannah Taylor, Grade 8*

I live on a tiny island called Mackinac Island. You pronounce it "MAC-en-aw," and it means "big **turtle**." Mackinac Island is on Lake Huron. It's only about thirteen kilometers around. A lot of really rich **tourists** used to come here. They built huge summer homes in West Bluff. These days, tourists still come here, but they aren't all rich. Mackinac is very quiet, and nothing has changed much in 100 years. Only 500 people live here. Cars are not allowed. People still walk or ride bikes everywhere, or they rent horse-drawn carriages. In fact, my school "bus" is a horse and **buggy**!

My mom and I don't live in a big house in West Bluff. We live downtown in an apartment. Mom has a toy shop, and the apartment is over it. I help her in the summer when there are lots of tourists. We call tourists "fudgies" because they always come here and buy **fudge**. I like chocolate fudge, but I don't eat as much as the tourists.

My cousin Erin thinks I'm lucky to live here. Sometimes I agree. Summers aren't too hot, and it's nice to have no traffic. But I don't always feel lucky. It's hard to remember the ferry and plane schedules to St. Ignace on the **mainland**. We're surrounded by water, but there aren't any good places to swim. Winters are very cold—it's often cold enough to freeze an ice bridge in the lake between Mackinac Island and St. Ignace. That's kind of fun, though. One person goes out and tests the ice bridge to make sure it's thick enough. Then we all walk across it to St. Ignace. Sometimes the ice bridge only lasts a few days, and sometimes it lasts two months. I used to ride my **snowmobile** to St. Ignace, but it took a long time and it was very cold, so now I save my allowance and take a little plane. It costs $24. There is actually a mall there, and some kids of my age.

My best friend Cherie and I complain about boys here. There are just 100 people in our school—that's kindergarten through Grade 12! My entire grade is only four girls and two boys. We sometimes meet tourists in the summer, but they don't stay here very long, so it's hard to make friends. I can't wait to go to college and see lots of people every day—and maybe get my **driver's license**!

Reading

1 Read the text and answer the questions.

1 What does "Mackinac" mean?
_____
2 What don't they allow on Mackinac Island?
_____
3 Why do Mackinac Islanders call tourists "fudgies"?
_____
_____
4 How did Hannah use to get to St. Ignace?
_____
_____
5 What do she and Cherie complain about?
_____
_____
6 Why is Hannah looking forward to college?
_____
_____

2 Match the captions to the photos.

1. We have a great time here when the lake freezes!

2. There are no cars, but people can ride in horse-drawn carriages.

3. They make a lot of fudge for the tourists.

4. Mackinac Island hasn't changed for about 150 years.

Vocabulary

3 Guess the meaning of these words and write a translation in your language. Then check in a dictionary.

1 turtle _____
2 tourist _____
3 buggy _____
4 fudge _____
5 mainland _____
6 snowmobile _____
7 driver's license _____

Project

4 Describe your ideal place to live.

I'd like to live in a(n) _____
(type of house/apartment/etc.) with a
_____ (yard?
roof garden? balcony? swimming pool?) in
_____
(name of city/town/state/country)
I'd like a _____
_____ (describe your ideal room)
with a view of _____
_____ (describe your ideal view).
I'd like to have a _____
_____ (name something
you'd like to own) in my house.
I'd like to live near a _____
_____ (finish this sentence).

Listening

1 Put the dialogue in the correct order. Number the sentences 1 to 6. Then listen and check your answers.

Because I'd like to travel all around the world and take pictures of interesting places. ☐

Yes. What job would you like to have? ☐

I'd like to be a photographer. ☐

What are you going to be? ☐

Why? ☐

Do you mean when I leave school? ☐

2 Listen to five teenagers talking about their ideal jobs. What do they all say? Write the correct letters in the boxes.

Who

a) wants to work with animals?
b) ~~would like to work for a television company?~~
c) is interested in science?
d) wants to be famous?
e) is really interested in food?
f) wants to study more but hasn't decided on a career?
g) comes from an international family?

1 Claudia [b]

2 Alex ☐

3 Natasha ☐

4 Will ☐

5 Sabina ☐

6 Andy ☐

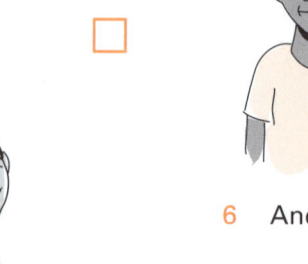

7 Emma ☐

Let's Check

Vocabulary check

1 Find the answers in the scrambled words below.

Who ...

1. works in a hospital? — nurse
2. cuts hair? — _____
3. cooks? — _____
4. must be a good rider? — _____
5. works with animals? — _____
6. designs buildings? — _____
7. works in a shop? — _____
8. writes for newspapers and magazines? — _____
9. speaks lots of languages? — _____
10. must be an excellent swimmer? — _____
11. works on a plane? — _____

- CHATRITEC • FECH • FELIDRAGU • YOCKEJ
- HARISERSERD • LEASS TISSANSTA • TEV
- RETERPRETIN • ~~RUSEN~~ • STURNOJALI
- THLIGF TADNTANET

Grammar check

2 Correct the mistake in each sentence.

- ◆ = there's a word missing
- N = change the order of two words
- X = change one word
- * = delete one word

1. We're going to the park meet Joanna. ◆
   We're going to the park to meet Joanna.
2. I didn't used to like swimming. X
   _____
3. We're staying in for to watch TV. *
   _____
4. I learned swim when I was three. ◆
   _____
5. Where you did use to go to school? N
   _____
6. I don't feel like to watching a video. *
   _____

3 Choose the correct words for each sentence.

1. She ____ live near us.
   A use   B use to   **C used to**
2. I don't mind ____ my room.
   A for cleaning   B clean   C cleaning
3. I used to ____ a sweet little dog.
   A had   B have   C having
4. It's really fun ____ swimming at night.
   A to go   B go   C for go
5. He's gone to the mall ____ for some new sneakers.
   A to look   B for looking   C for to look
6. It's impossible ____ fast up this hill.
   A biking   B bike   C to bike
7. Did your mother ____ to be a flight attendant?
   A use   B used   C using
8. I'm staying up late ____ the World Cup on TV.
   A for watch   B to watch   C for watching
9. Did she hate ____ in the school concert?
   A singing   B she sings   C sing
10. She still hasn't finished ____ her room.
    A paint   B painting   C to paint
11. My brother is hoping ____ a famous movie star one day!
    A be   B being   C to be

4 Make sentences by putting the words in order.

1. enjoy / I / meeting / new / people / really
   I really enjoy meeting new people.
2. and chocolate / eating / given up / I've / candy
   _____
3. at / exciting / It's / look / stars / the / to
   _____
4. a / Did / farm / have / horse / to / use / you / on your / ?
   _____
5. bus / catch / first / getting / the / to / up early / We're
   _____
6. be / day / like / one / rich / to / Would / you / ?
   _____

UNIT 6

Practice

Edison—the world's greatest inventor

Thomas Alva Edison was born in 1847 in Milan, Ohio. He was one of seven children. He first went to school at the age of eight, but he didn't do very well. The teacher didn't realize that he was slightly deaf, and thought he was stupid. In fact, the teacher told Edison he was stupid, and the poor boy ran home crying to his mother. He went back to school from time to time until the age of twelve, but received most of his education from his mother. He also taught himself a lot—he was an enthusiastic reader of science books.

As soon as he left school, he got a job selling newspapers on the street. He immediately showed his intelligence and business sense on the job. Each day, he read the news stories before he took the newspapers from the shop: when they were interesting, he picked up a lot of papers—when they were less interesting, he picked up a smaller number. With this simple trick, he made much more money than the other newspaper boys.

Edison's first invention appeared when he was only nineteen. He then started work as a full-time inventor, creating new machines or improving machines that already existed. For example, Alexander Graham Bell invented the telephone in 1876, but later Edison made a new and much better microphone for it.

In 1877, Edison produced the first sound-recording machine, called the "phonograph." It was the first step toward today's cassettes and CDs—so remember Edison the next time you listen to your favorite album! Two years later, he invented the light bulb. New York became the first city in the world with electric lighting.

In the late 1880s, he produced a movie camera and projector—the Kinetograph and the Kinetoscope. So he was also one of the fathers of the movie industry. At the same time, he invented electrical batteries, to use with his new cameras.

Altogether, more than 1,000 inventions came out of Edison's laboratory. When he died in 1931, the lights were switched off all over the USA as a tribute.

Reading

1 Read the text and answer the questions.

1. How many brothers and sisters did Edison have?
   _____

2. Why did he run home from school?
   _____
   _____

3. At what age did he leave school?
   _____

4. Who was his best teacher?
   _____

5. How old was Edison when he started inventing?
   _____

6. What improvement did he make for the telephone?
   _____
   _____

7. What was the "phonograph"?
   _____
   _____

8. In which year did he invent the light bulb?
   _____

9. What was Edison's contribution to the movie industry?
   _____
   _____

10. How many things did Edison invent?
    _____

11. Which of his inventions do you think was the most important? Why?
    _____
    _____

12. What would you most like to invent yourself?
    _____
    _____

Writing

2 Write the questions and answers for the following dialogue. A is a reporter and is interviewing B, a successful writer, about his/her life.

A Ask B where he/she lives.
_____

B Give your answer.
_____

A Ask B when he/she wrote his/her first book.
_____
_____

B Answer B and also give the name of the book.
_____

A Ask B how long it took to write it.
_____
_____

B Give your answer.
_____

A Ask B about the best part of the job.
_____
_____

B Give your answer.
_____

A Ask B about his/her free-time activities.
_____
_____

B Give your answer.
_____
_____

UNIT 7 House contents

Vocabulary

1 Match the words to the numbers.

freezer	4	microwave	__
coffee machine	__	stereo	__
stove	__	oven	__
pillow	__	sink	__
dishwasher	__	sofa	__
blinds	__	faucet	__
fridge	__	toaster	__
teapot	__	washing machine	__

Dialogue work

2 Complete the dialogue with the sentences.

Guest (1) _I'd like to book a room for two nights, please._

Receptionist Would you like a single room or a double?

Guest (2) _____

Receptionist For how many nights?

Guest (3) _____

Receptionist When is this for?

Guest (4) _____
_____

Receptionist A double room is $90 per night.

Guest (5) _____

Receptionist Yes, it is.

Guest (6) _____

Receptionist I'm afraid pets aren't allowed in this hotel.

Guest (7) _____
_____

Receptionist I'm very sorry. Animals are not allowed in any part of the hotel.

- Is breakfast included?
- It's only a little dog. And he's always very good.
- I'd like a double room.
- ~~I'd like to book a room for two nights, please.~~
- Is it okay to bring my dog?
- May 23rd and 24th. How much will it be?
- Two.

Grammar practice

3 Join the sentences using *who* or *that*.

1. *Smash* is a new magazine. It has articles and stories about musicians.
   Smash is a new magazine that has articles and stories about musicians.
2. Jeff Probst is a TV announcer. He got famous with the TV show *Survivor*.
   _____
   _____
   _____
3. *Endz* is a new computer game. It makes you think.
   _____
   _____
4. The Lola 230 is a new cell phone. It can take and send photos.
   _____
   _____
5. On City Tours, we have wonderful tour guides. They really know New York.
   _____
   _____
   _____
6. *Fizzit* is a new drink. It's good for your teeth.
   _____
   _____
7. On Sky Air, we have great flight attendants. They will be happy to help you.
   _____
   _____
   _____
8. *Beach* is a new perfume. It smells like the ocean.
   _____
   _____
9. Patrick Swayze is an amazing dancer. He starred in the movie *Dirty Dancing*.
   _____
   _____
   _____

4 Complete the sentences with *who* or *that*.

1. I know a girl _who_ lives on a houseboat.
2. Do you like movies _____ make you laugh?
3. The people _____ live in that house own a race horse.
4. Do you remember the people _____ used to live next door?
5. She bought a pair of sneakers _____ cost $100.
6. A jockey is a person _____ rides horses in races.
7. There's a shop opposite my house _____ sells really cheap CDs.
8. A vegetarian is a person _____ doesn't eat meat.
9. Animals _____ eat meat are called carnivores.

5 Complete the sentences with *whose* or *where*.

1. We usually go to a beach _where_ you can go waterskiing.
2. There's a boy in my class _____ mother is a TV announcer.
3. Let's go to a café _____ you can sit outside.
4. Do you know that movie theater _____ you can get really cheap popcorn?
5. I have really small feet. I don't know anybody _____ shoes fit me.
6. A place _____ you keep horses is a stable.
7. I know someone _____ brother was in the Olympic Games.

Study Tip

Learning useful phrases

In your vocabulary book keep a list of phrases which are useful or which you particularly like.
For example:
anyway	used after an interruption
well	to introduce what you're going to say; to give you time while you think about what you're going to say
hang on	when you've just had a good idea; when you want someone to wait

UNIT 7

UNIT 7

> When *that* or *who* refers to the object of the sentence, we can leave it out.
> We can say:
> *I can't find the magazine **that** I bought yesterday.*
> Or: *I can't find the magazine I bought yesterday.*
> We can say:
> *There's the girl **who** we saw in the park yesterday.*
> Or: *There's the girl we saw in the park yesterday.*

6 Put brackets ( ) around *that* or *who* if they can be left out. Underline them if they can't.

1 Did you like that boy (who) we met at the tennis court?
2 I like books that make me laugh.
3 I saw the people who live next door to you.
4 We're listening to the CD that Dave left here.
5 Can I borrow the shirt that you bought yesterday?
6 She's somebody who goes to my karate class.
7 Have you tried the chocolates that we bought?
8 Who was that girl who you called a minute ago?

7 Make one sentence from two using *who* or *that* each time. If it is possible to leave out *who* or *that*, write them in brackets ( ).

1 Who was that boy? He came here a minute ago.
Who was that boy who came here a minute ago?

2 Can you wash the cup? You've just used it.
Can you wash the cup (that) you've just used?

3 Did you know that old lady? We helped her in the grocery store.
_____
_____

4 Let's look at the magazines. You bought them yesterday.
_____
_____

8 Put the verbs in the present simple passive.

1 These sneakers _are made_ (make) in the Philippines.
2 German _____ (not teach) at our school.
3 I _____ (expect) to help with the dishes.
4 You _____ (not allow) to use your cell phone at school.
5 The glasses _____ (keep) in the middle cabinet.

9 Complete the sentences with the correct verb in the present simple passive.

> translate   make   read   keep   ~~play~~

1 Soccer _is played_ all over the world.
2 The Harry Potter books _____ into many languages.
3 This newspaper _____ by four million people every day.
4 Cheese _____ from milk.
5 Animals in zoos _____ in cages.

5 I didn't see the man. He took Mark's wallet at the bus stop.
_____
_____

6 I like that singer. He was talking on the radio this morning.
_____
_____

7 Did you like the CDs? Emma gave them to you.
_____
_____

8 We didn't see the waiter. Your parents know him.
_____
_____

10 Complete the fact file. Then rewrite the sentences in the passive, leaving out the words in brackets.

THE BEST OF WHERE YOU LIVE

1 (They) show all the latest movies at the _Astoria Theater_. **(Name a movie theater.)**
2 (You) eat the best food in _____ **(Name an area of your country.)**
3 (They) make the best cheese in _____ **(Name an area of your country.)**
4 (They) play the best music on _____ **(Name a radio station.)**
5 (They) serve the biggest pizzas at _____ **(Name a restaurant.)**
6 (They) sell the most expensive clothes at _____ **(Name a shop.)**
7 (They) show the funniest TV shows on _____ **(Name a TV channel.)**

1 _All the latest movies are shown at the Astoria Theater._
2 _____
3 _____
4 _____
5 _____
6 _____
7 _____

11 Match the question phrases to the answers. Then write questions with *Where*, *When*, or *What* and answers in the present simple passive.

1 baseball (play)? d
2 kangaroos (find)? ☐
3 the computers (keep)? ☐
4 paella (eat)? ☐
5 Porsche cars (make)? ☐
6 lunch (serve)? ☐
7 your kittens (name)? ☐
8 the rooms (clean)? ☐
9 baby sheep (call)? ☐

a) at one o'clock
b) Fifi and Toto
c) in Germany
d) ~~in the U.S.~~
e) in Spain
f) every day at ten
g) lambs
h) in Australia
i) in Room 28

1 Q: _Where is baseball played?_
  A: _It's played in the U.S._
2 Q: _____
  A: _____
3 Q: _____
  A: _____
4 Q: _____
  A: _____
5 Q: _____
  A: _____
6 Q: _____
  A: _____
7 Q: _____
  A: _____
8 Q: _____
  A: _____
9 Q: _____
  A: _____

UNIT 7
Skills Development

☐ We spent our time on the beach relaxing and watching other people.

☐ On our last night, we stopped in a village where there was a *ceilidh* (that's pronounced "kay-lee"). A family of musicians was playing. One of them was playing a *bodhran*. We all joined in and learned some traditional Irish singing and dancing.

[1] We had an amazing week in Ireland last summer. We flew to Cork and hired a traditional caravan with a horse to pull it!

☐ The horse was named Caramel, and we soon made friends with her. We traveled around very slowly. When there was a steep hill, we had to get out and walk.

☐ When I wasn't watching people on the beach, I was trying the local snacks. My favorite was cold coconut milk. It's served in a coconut with a straw. I also liked the fresh shrimp that are grilled on the beach and served with lime juice. Mmmm … perfect for lunch after a long swim.

☐ It was definitely the best vacation we've ever had. But two weeks wasn't enough for all those islands. One day I'll go back and stay longer and maybe learn to speak a few words of the local language.

☐ At night, Caramel slept in fields, and we slept in the caravan. It had everything we needed. There were beds, a stove, a fridge, and maps that we used all the time. Unfortunately, Caramel sometimes didn't want to follow the route that we chose.

☐ In our second week, we flew from Honolulu to The Big Island. It's the biggest of the islands, and there's a huge variety of things to see. We went on an expedition to Kilauea, the largest active volcano in the world, and we also rented masks and snorkels and went snorkeling on the coral reef.

[A] Last year, our whole family went on vacation to Hawaii for two weeks. We spent our first week in a hotel at Waikiki Beach.

☐ The next day, we flew back to Miami. I will never forget that wonderful week when I learned about traveling the old-fashioned way—with a horse!

1 ☐

2 ☐

3 ☐

4 ☐

Reading

1 The articles in a travel magazine are mixed up.

a) **Read the paragraphs marked 1 and A. Which two countries are the articles about?**
_____
_____

b) **Read the rest of the two articles. Separate them and put the paragraphs in order by labeling them 1 to 5 and A to E.**

2 Match the captions to the photos.

a) Kilauea, the largest active volcano in the world
b) A horse pulled our traditional gypsy caravan.
c) We explored the coral reefs.
d) They played some traditional Irish music.

Vocabulary

3 Find words for the following in the text.

1 an Irish party _____
2 an Irish musical instrument _____
3 You can wear it over your eyes and nose when you swim underwater. _____
4 You get air through it when you're underwater. _____
5 a type of seafood _____
6 a tropical drink _____
7 You drink through it. _____

Listening

6 Listen and write the missing word in each sentence. Then listen to another sentence and guess the meaning of the missing word. Write a translation in your language.

Sentence

1 What are you doing with that _____ ?
2 Do we have to put _____ on the table?
3 This TV has a really wide _____ .
4 I'm trying to _____ this flashlight.
5 Can you _____ the cabinet door, please?
6 Can I have a _____ , please?

Translation

_____
_____
_____
_____
_____
_____

Study Tip

4 When you don't understand a word, don't stop reading or listening. The meaning often comes after the word. Guess the meaning of these words. Write the translation next to them.

1 There wasn't any *soap* (_____) in the bathroom, so I couldn't wash my hands.
2 Can I have the *scissors* (_____)? I want to cut my hair.
3 I can't stop *yawning* (_____). I'm really sleepy.
4 Can you buy me a roll of *film* (_____) for my camera? I've taken 32 pictures, so this one is nearly finished.
5 The *brakes* (_____) on my bike didn't work, so I couldn't stop.

Writing

5 Write a travel article in your notebook about one of your best vacations. Include some of these points.

- Where did you go?
- Who with?
- For how long?
- Where did you stay?
- What was the hotel/house like?
- What did you do every day?
- What was the food like?
- What was the weather like?
- Did you go on expeditions?
- Why was the vacation really good?

UNIT 7

UNIT 7

Talk Time

1 Write the correct phrases in the speech balloons.

- I've brought a friend along.
- Nice to meet you.
- Let's get started.
- Nice to meet you, too.

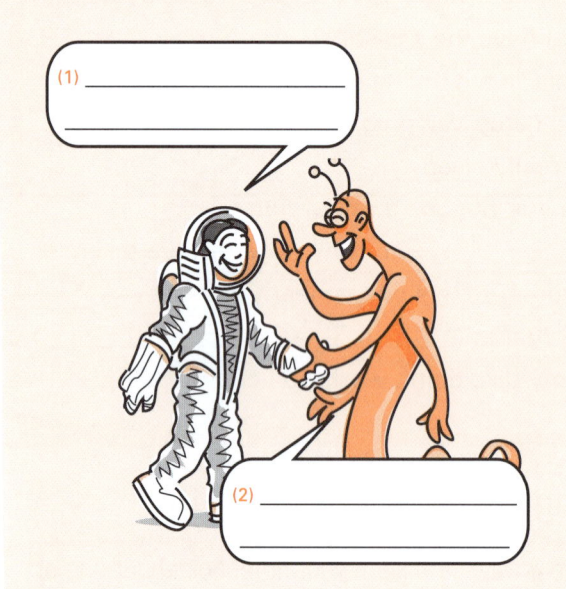

(1) _____

(2) _____

(3) _____

(4) _____

2 Complete the dialogue with the phrases.

- I'm afraid
- I'm afraid not.
- By the way
- Wait
- Maybe
- What kind of

Customer I'm looking for a present for my little sister. I'd like to buy her a stuffed animal.

Assistant (1) _____ stuffed animal?

Customer I don't want to get her a teddy bear. She already has 26 teddy bears. (2) _____ a dolphin.

Assistant (3) _____ I don't have any dolphins.

Customer What about a giraffe or a hippopotamus?

Assistant (4) _____

Customer Do you have a parrot?

Assistant Yes. (5) _____ just a second and I'll go and get you one.

Customer Wow! It's enormous. I really like it. Yes, I'll take the parrot, please.

Assistant Okay, I'll put it in a bag for you. (6) _____ , if it won't stop talking, just take the batteries out.

Let's Check

Vocabulary check

1 Match the words to the clues.

> blinds pillows dishwasher freezer
> fridge microwave stereo ~~oven~~ sink
> faucets washing machine

1. You make cakes in it. — _oven_
2. You keep cold drinks in it. — _____
3. You keep ice cream in it. — _____
4. It washes your clothes. — _____
5. It washes your dishes. — _____
6. You have them over windows. — _____
7. Water comes out of them. — _____
8. It cooks food very fast. — _____
9. You can wash dishes or vegetables in it. — _____
10. You put them on chairs or sofas. — _____
11. You use it to play CDs. — _____

Grammar check

2 Correct the mistake in each sentence.

> ◆ = there's a word missing
> N = change the order of two words
> X = change one word
> * = delete one word

1. What they are called? **N**
   What are they called?
2. Where is these jeans made? **X**
   _____
3. Let's go to a café we can have milkshakes. ◆
   _____
4. Have you seen the man whose goes to work on a skateboard? **X**
   _____
5. Do you know the people who they own that boat? *
   _____
6. I really like that girl lives in the apartment next door. ◆
   _____

3 Choose the correct words for each sentence.

1. The trash ____ once a week.
   A picked up **B** is picked up **C** are picked up
2. All the grades ____ in the teacher's notebook.
   A wrote **B** writing **C** are written
3. She likes the purse ____ you bought her in Florence.
   A when **B** whose **C** that
4. Where is the computer ____?
   A keeping **B** keep **C** kept
5. You ____ allowed to eat candy in class.
   A not **B** aren't **C** don't
6. There's the boy ____ the guitar at the club.
   A whose played **B** played **C** who played
7. I have a friend ____ father is a pilot.
   A that **B** whose **C** where
8. We're going to the hotel ____ we stayed last year.
   A whose **B** that **C** where
9. ____ expected to clean my room once a week.
   A I'm **B** It **C** I'll
10. Did you know the boy ____ spoke to in the park?
    A when we **B** what we **C** we
11. Can I have the books ____ gave you last week?
    A what I **B** I **C** when I

4 Make sentences by putting the words in order.

1. Breakfast / from / is / nine / served / seven / until
   Breakfast is served from seven until nine.
2. are / at / do / expected / home / to / What / you / ?
   _____
3. all / CDs / He's / him / I / let / lost / the / that / him borrow
   _____
4. a beach / can / go / Let's / to / we / where / windsurf
   _____
5. anyone / are / Do / famous / know / parents / whose / you / ?
   _____

UNIT 8
Injury and illness

Vocabulary

1 Read the text, then write the correct name under each picture.

It's a bad day at the sports club. Eleven people have problems.
- Andy's leg is bleeding.
- Ben has broken his arm.
- Fran has a cold.
- Sue has a fever.
- Larry has a toothache.
- Samantha has a sore throat.
- Serena has a headache.
- Dan has a stomachache.
- Erica feels dizzy.
- Rob has hurt his knee.
- ~~Hannah has sprained her wrist.~~

1. Hannah   2. _____   3. _____
4. _____   5. _____   6. _____
7. _____   8. _____   9. _____
10. _____ 11. _____

Dialogue work

2 Complete the dialogue with the correct words.

> brown   call   competition   dishwasher   farm
> games   horse   thousand   what   ~~won~~

Adam What would you do if you (1) _won_ lots of money?

Dominic You mean in a (2) _____ or something?

Adam Yes. What would you do if you won a (3) _____ dollars, for example?

Dominic I'd buy a (4) _____ for my mom. Then I'd never have to do the dishes again.

Adam But (5) _____ would you get for yourself?

Dominic I'd buy a (6) _____ I think. I could keep it on Jon's (7) _____ , maybe.

Adam Cool. Then we could all go over to Jon's and ride it. What would you (8) _____ it?

Dominic If it was a white horse, I'd call it Starlight. If it was (9) _____ , I'd call it Choco. What would you do?

Adam I'd probably buy season tickets for the Philadelphia Eagles. Then I could go and watch all their (10) _____ .

Study Tip

English spelling

English words aren't always spelled as they sound, e.g. *cough*, *right*, *straight*, *ghost*. Try to develop a visual memory for words.

Here's an idea to help you:

look at a word, then cover it and try to write it.

Grammar practice

3 Choose the correct word in each sentence.

1. *Anybody / Somebody* has eaten all my chocolates. [Somebody circled]
2. We were too far from the stage. We didn't see *nothing / anything*.
3. He isn't happy at the moment. He's worried about *something / anything*.
4. Hello? Is *everybody / anybody* there? Hello?
5. I hate this place. There are spiders *everywhere / anywhere*.
6. Just stay here for a minute. Don't go *anywhere / nowhere*.
7. *Somebody / Everybody* really enjoyed the picnic.
8. *Something / Anything* strange is happening. What is going on?
9. There's *nothing / something* you can do to help. So just sit down and relax.

4 Complete the sentences with pronouns beginning *some-, any-, every-,* or *no-*.

1. "What do you want to do tomorrow?" "_Anything_. I don't mind. You choose."
2. I don't want _____ to eat, thanks. I feel sick.
3. I heard a voice. I think there's _____ in the garden.
4. There's _____ in this envelope. I think it's a CD.
5. This village is boring. There's _____ to do and _____ to go.
6. Your room is a mess. There are old magazines and socks _____ .
7. _____ in my family likes snakes. We're all scared of them.
8. Let's go _____ sunny this summer. I'm fed up with the rain.
9. I'm not going to go to the party. I won't know _____ there.
10. I don't want to go _____ this evening. I'm tired.

5 Match the people to what they said. Then report their requests using *told* or *asked*.

1. [d] The doctor _told me to open my mouth and say "Aaah."_
2. [f] My little sister _asked me to help her with her math._
3. [ ] The dentist _____
4. [ ] My pen pal _____
5. [ ] The photographer _____
6. [ ] My friends _____
7. [ ] The soccer coach _____
8. [ ] My teacher _____
9. [ ] My mother _____
10. [ ] The man at the check-in desk _____

a) Please take Truffles for a walk.
b) Go immediately to Gate 25.
c) Brush your teeth after every meal.
d) ~~Open your mouth and say "Aaah."~~
e) Do Exercise 3 again.
f) ~~Please help me with my math.~~
g) Please bring some CDs to our party.
h) Look at the camera and say "Cheese."
i) Stay near the goal.
j) Please send a photo of you and your family.

UNIT 8

6 Match the sentence beginnings with the commands. Then complete each sentence with the correct reported command.

1. [f] Mom and Dad were asleep, so I told _Jack not to play the guitar._
2. [ ] It was a dangerous road, so I told _____
3. [ ] It was a secret, so I told _____
4. [ ] My camera was broken, so I asked _____
5. [ ] I was really hungry, so I asked _____
6. [ ] I was in a bad mood, so I told _____
7. [ ] I felt dizzy, so I asked _____

a) Ben, don't ask me silly questions.
b) Chloe, don't eat any of my chips.
c) Dad, can you repair it?
d) Hannah, don't drive too fast.
e) Christine, can you get me a glass of water?
f) ~~Jack, don't play the guitar.~~
g) Seth, don't tell anyone.

7 Match the sentence halves and write the complete sentence.

1. [c] If he had enough money, _he'd buy a new guitar._
2. [ ] If she ate more fruit and vegetables, _____
3. [ ] The town would be cleaner _____
4. [ ] If you had a computer, _____
5. [ ] If I were you, _____
6. [ ] It would be great _____
7. [ ] She wouldn't like it _____

a) I wouldn't listen to Alison.
b) if I won this competition.
c) ~~he'd buy a new guitar.~~
d) she'd be healthier.
e) if there weren't any cars.
f) if you read her diary.
g) you could send me e-mails.

8 Write sentences in the second conditional using the verbs in brackets.

1. If I _had_ (have) lots of money, I _would buy_ (buy) a new skateboard.
2. He _____ (look) better if he sometimes _____ (comb) his hair.
3. We _____ (not have) to do the dishes if we _____ (have) a dishwasher.
4. What _____ (you like) to be if you _____ (can) choose any job in the world?
5. I _____ (not go) see that movie if I _____ (be) you.
6. If I _____ (know) Patrick's number, I _____ (call) him now.
7. If you _____ (have) one wish, what _____ (you ask) for?
8. I _____ (prefer) our school if we _____ (not have) to wear this boring gray uniform.
9. Your cat _____ (catch) mice if you _____ (not feed) it so much cat food.

66

9 Complete the second conditional sentences.

1 If I met <u>Michael Jordan, I'd ask him to play basketball with me.</u>
2 If I could have any job, I'd be _____
3 If I had a lot of money, _____
4 If I could go anywhere in the world, _____
5 If I had _____
6 If I were _____

10 Complete the quiz questions. Then choose an answer and write it with *I'd*.

THE MEGA HORROR QUIZ
Are you a cool cat or a nervous mouse? Find out with this quiz!

1 What would you do if you <u>couldn't</u> (can't) find the way out of a dark forest?
 a) cry
 b) wait for someone to come and find me
 c) (call my mom on my cell phone)
 <u>I'd call my mom on my cell phone.</u>

2 What would you do if there _____ (be) a ghost in your bedroom?
 a) cry
 b) hide under the bed
 c) tell it to go away
 _____

3 What would you do if a bull _____ (run) toward you in a field?
 a) run away
 b) sit down on the grass
 c) jump on it and ride it
 _____

4 What would you do if you _____ (cut) your finger badly?
 a) cry
 b) call an ambulance
 c) show it to my parents
 _____

5 What would you do if you _____ (find) a big spider in your shoe?
 a) call the police
 b) call the zoo
 c) take a picture of it
 _____

6 What would you do if you _____ (drop) your father's expensive camera on the floor?
 a) say nothing
 b) say sorry
 c) start saving my allowance
 _____

7 What would you do if you _____ (wake) up and you _____ (can't) remember your name?
 a) stay in bed for the day
 b) ask a friend about my name
 c) choose a nice new name
 _____

Score 1 point for a) answers.
Score 2 points for b) answers.
Score 3 points for c) answers.

Analysis

15–18: Cool cat! You can always see a way out of every difficult situation. People think you are a very exciting person.

10–14: You're Mr. or Ms. Sensible. You're a kind person and you understand people's problems. But your life would be more fun if you had a little more courage.

6–9: Nervous mouse! You're scared of everything. Be careful of this book. It might fall off the table and hurt your foot!

CULTURE SPOT

HAWAII

Hawaii, a **chain** of islands in the Pacific Ocean, is famous for its spectacular beaches, its volcanoes, its fabulous sunsets, and its friendly people. It has good weather and warm water all year. They say it's always sunny somewhere on the islands. It has some of the best surfing in the world. So it's not surprising that it's a very popular vacation spot.

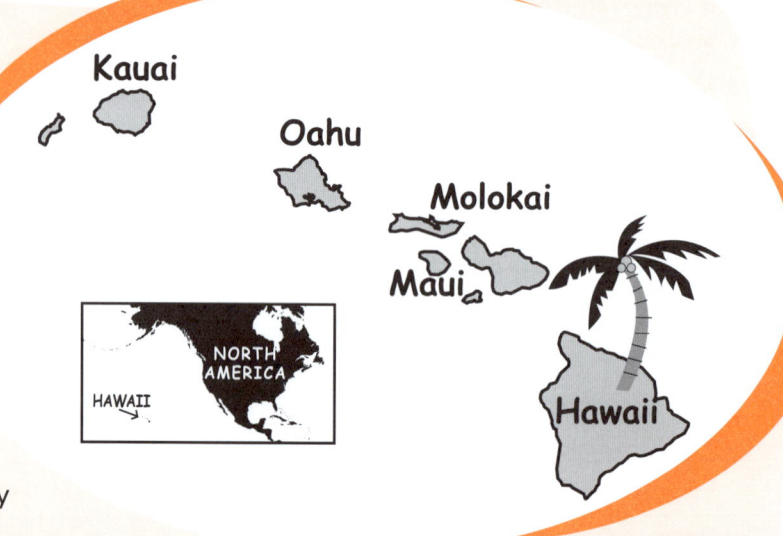

Tourism hasn't always been big in Hawaii. The first people to live there were probably Polynesians from Tahiti. Europeans didn't visit the islands until the eighteenth century. Then **whalers** came from all over the world in the nineteenth century. They liked the warm weather and tropical fruit such as **pineapple**, guava, and **coconut**. Later, travelers and **traders** from Japan, China, Australia, and the United States came. Today, you can fly 3,378km southwest of San Francisco and be there in about three hours.

Hawaii became America's 50th state in 1959. Hawaiians still have their own culture and language. There are only twelve letters in their alphabet: a, e, h, i, k, l, m, n, o, p, u, and w. But that doesn't mean the language is easy to learn. For instance, the longest word in Hawaiian is *humuhumunukunukuapua'a*. It's the name of a fish, and it means "fish with a pig's nose." Most Hawaiians just call it the "humu." Hawaiian children often learn the hula when they're very young. A hula is a dance that tells a story. It is usually about a hero or a **chief**. And all Hawaiians enjoy "luaus"—beach parties with dancers, storytellers, and singers. Luaus used to be just for important people, but now any visitor to Hawaii can take part and try the roast pig and other food.

Hawaii used to make money from fruit **plantations** and fishing. These are still important, but its biggest industries today are **sugarcane processing**, coffee, and, above all, tourism.

Reading

1 Read the text and write T (true) or F (false).

1. You can go surfing in Hawaii. ___
2. Not many people visit Hawaii. ___
3. People in Hawaii only speak English. ___
4. Only adults learn the hula. ___
5. There isn't a fruit industry in Hawaii anymore. ___

Vocabulary

2 Match the meanings to the words.

1. chain — f
2. whaler — ☐
3. pineapple — ☐
4. coconut — ☐
5. trader — ☐
6. chief — ☐
7. plantation — ☐
8. sugarcane — ☐
9. process (*verb*) — ☐

a) a person who buys and sells
b) a big farm that grows just one thing
c) a leader
d) a tall plant that is used for making sugar
e) a large tropical fruit that's sweet and yellow inside
f) ~~a group or line~~
g) a tropical fruit with sweet milk inside
h) to put through machines
i) a person who catches whales

Project

4 Write about a tourist area or town in your country. List six interesting places to visit and write a sentence about each one. Use the list on this page as a model.

Reading

3 Read about some places to visit in Hawaii. Match four of the places to the photos. Write the numbers in the boxes next to the photos.

6 Places to visit in Hawaii

1 Haleakala Crater
This volcanic mountain looks like the surface of the moon.

2 Hanauma Bay
You can go snorkeling and see awesome fish.

3 Dole Pineapple Plantation
See how pineapples are grown, ride a train, and find your way out of the maze.

4 Alii Gardens Marketplace
Shop right across from the ocean for everything from coffee beans to sandals.

5 Diamond Head
Climb to the top for a great view of the city of Honolulu.

6 Fern Grotto
Plants grow from the cave ceilings in Kauai. Scientists say these caves are millions of years old!

6 Places to Visit in _____

1. _____
2. _____
3. _____
4. _____
5. _____
6. _____

Listening

1 Listen and complete the information board.

A (1) _FISHING_ **TRIP**

NAME OF BOAT: (2) _____
THE TRIP LASTS: (3) _____
WE GIVE YOU: (4) _____
PRICE PER PERSON: (5) _____
BOAT LEAVES AT: (6) _____

2 Listen and complete the information board.

Nantucket Bike Rentals

Price per day: (1) _____
A day is from: (2) _____ a.m.
to (3) _____ p.m.
Deposit: (4) _____
We will give you a free (5) _____ rental.

Let's Check

Vocabulary check

1 Choose the correct word for each sentence.

> bleeding ~~broken~~ hurt ill sore

1 Sue came back from her skiing vacation with a <u>broken</u> wrist. Now she can't ride her bike for six weeks.
2 Actors and singers often get _____ throats because they use their voices a lot.
3 I always feel _____ when I travel by bus.
4 Lily's hand is _____ . She did it with a knife when she was cutting up onions.
5 My legs _____ today because we went on a three-hour walk yesterday.

Grammar check

2 Correct the mistake in each sentence.

> ◆ = there's a word missing
> N = change the order of two words
> X = change one word
> * = delete one word

1 I didn't meet nobody nice at the party. **X**
   <u>I didn't meet anybody nice at the party.</u>
2 If I were you, I wouldn't to eat that yogurt. *
   _____
3 Melissa asked me wait for her. ◆
   _____
4 I think Orlando is anywhere in the United States. **X**
   _____
5 The team captain told us not stay up late the night before the game. ◆
   _____
6 Which videos you would buy if you had the money? **N**
   _____

3 Choose the correct words for each sentence.

1 _____ in my class likes sending e-mails and messages. We all do it on our lunch breaks.
   A Nobody   **B** Somebody   **(C) Everybody**
2 There's _____ in my class who can move his ears up and down.
   A somebody   **B** anybody   **C** everybody
3 My parents always tell me _____ a bike helmet.
   A wearing   **B** to wear   **C** to wearing
4 Football is his life. _____ is more important to him.
   A Something   **B** Anything   **C** Nothing
5 I told you _____ in the bag under my bed.
   A not look   **B** not looking   **C** not to look
6 Let's go somewhere else. _____ in this shop is too expensive.
   A Something   **B** Anything   **C** Everything
7 If I _____ $1,000, I would buy lots of new clothes.
   A win   **B** will win   **C** won
8 I'm not going _____ today. I'm cold and tired, and I want to stay at home.
   A nowhere   **B** anywhere   **C** everywhere

4 Make sentences by putting the words in order.

1 anything / drink / eat / like / or / to / Would / you / ?
   <u>Would you like anything to eat or drink?</u>
2 party / pajamas / to my / to / told / wear / Who / you / ?
   _____
3 asked me / the costumes / help her / Melanie / to / for the play / with
   _____
4 a / Everyone / helmet / should / they bike / wear / when
   _____
5 to Alex / any / I / If / lend / money / were / wouldn't / you
   _____

UNIT **8**

UNIT 8 Practice

Reading

1 Read the article about tea. Are the sentences right (A) or wrong (B)? If there is not enough information to answer "Right" or "Wrong," choose "Doesn't say" (C).

A nice cup of tea!

Americans drink 350 million cups of coffee a day. But in Britain, tea is the most popular drink. At least 77% of British people drink three or four cups of tea a day. More than 185 million cups of tea are drunk every day in Britain. A lot of British people drink tea first with breakfast, then at eleven o'clock, then with lunch, then at four o'clock, then at dinner time, and finally just before bed. Only 23% of British people drink coffee more often than tea.

Most people use tea bags to make tea, but some serious tea drinkers still make tea in the traditional way. First the water is boiled. Then some of the boiling water is used to make the teapot warm. Then the tea leaves are put in the teapot. Then the boiling water is added. Then the pot is left for five minutes under a "tea cozy." A tea cozy is a sort of jacket that keeps the teapot warm. Finally, the tea is served in delicate cups with saucers.

The word "tea" is used in a lot of different ways in the English language. A lot of people in Britain call their dinner their "tea," even if they don't drink tea with it. If someone is upset, they need "tea and sympathy." And there's the expression "a storm in a teacup." It means that people are making trouble about something that isn't important.

1 Most British people drink tea every day.
  (A) Right   B Wrong   C Doesn't say
2 British people never drink tea after dinner.
  A Right   B Wrong   C Doesn't say
3 British people make bad coffee.
  A Right   B Wrong   C Doesn't say
4 Tea made with tea bags is not very good.
  A Right   B Wrong   C Doesn't say
5 You use cold water to make tea.
  A Right   B Wrong   C Doesn't say
6 Most people in Britain drink tea with milk and sugar.
  A Right   B Wrong   C Doesn't say
7 A tea cozy helps to keep the teapot warm.
  A Right   B Wrong   C Doesn't say
8 Some people call dinner "tea."
  A Right   B Wrong   C Doesn't say
9 "A storm in a teacup" means the weather is very bad.
  A Right   B Wrong   C Doesn't say

2 Read the article about teddy bears. Choose the best word (A, B, or C) for each space.

You probably know (1) ____ teddy bears are the world's most popular toys. But you might not know that they are also (2) ____ most collectable toys. Collectors buy (3) ____ sell teddy bears all over the world. Unusual teddy bears (4) ____ be very valuable. The (5) ____ price that anyone has paid so far is $200,000. That was in 2000 for a bear (6) ____ Teddy Girl.

Are you feeling upset now because you (7) ____ thrown away all your old teddy bears? Well, (8) ____ worry too much! Most teddy bears (9) ____ not valuable. To be valuable, teddy bears (10) ____ to be more than 40 years old. There's no point buying new bears. You will have (11) ____ a very long time before they are valuable. It (12) ____ better if you asked your grandmother about her teddy bears. She might have a valuable one (13) ____ in her house!

1 A because   (B) that   C a
2 A some   B for   C the
3 A for   B and   C so
4 A can   B are   C always
5 A higher   B high   C highest
6 A call   B name's   C called
7 A have   B did   C were
8 A no   B must   C don't
9 A was   B will   C are
10 A must   B have   C will
11 A waiting   B wait   C to wait
12 A will be   B would be   C was
13 A nowhere   B somewhere   C everywhere

Writing

3 Complete the letter. Write ONE word for each space.

Dear Andrea,
Would you like (1) _____ come to my Halloween party (2) _____ Saturday? It's going to be (3) _____ my house from 7 p.m. (4) _____ 9 p.m. We (5) _____ going to wear Halloween costumes and (6) _____ some Halloween games. Do you (7) _____ any scary music on CDs (8) _____ cassettes? Elliot and Laurie (9) _____ coming, and so (10) _____ Vicky. I think it will (11) _____ a lot of fun. I hope you can come. Let me know.
Suzie

Listening

4 Listen to five short conversations. Check (✔) the right answers.

1 What time does the movie start?
   6:15 A ☐   6:30 B ✔   6:45 C ☐

2 How many people were at the rehearsal?
   33 A ☐   30 B ☐   13 C ☐

3 Which table do they buy?
   A ☐   B ☐   C ☐

4 What has she bought?
   A ☐   B ☐   C ☐

5 How much were the tickets?
   $50 A ☐ $15 B ☐ $60 C ☐

5 Listen to Maria talking to her friend about a visit to Mexico. Circle A, B, or C.

1 Maria is going to Mexico next
   A month.
   B year.
   C week. (circled)

2 She's staying
   A in a hotel.
   B with a family.
   C in a school.

3 She's going by
   A plane.
   B train.
   C bus.

4 The family lives
   A in the center.
   B in Acapulco.
   C near the airport.

5 They'll meet Maria and
   A go home by car.
   B walk home.
   C go home by bus.

6 Maria wants to buy them
   A fortune cookies.
   B a CD.
   C a book.

6 You will hear some information about a museum. Listen and complete the sign.

Museum of Science

Summer opening
From: (1) _May 1_   To: (2) _____
On: Monday, (3) _____ , and (4) _____

Opening times
From: (5) _____ a.m.   To: (6) _____ p.m.

Prices
Adults: (7) _____   Children: (8) _____

For more information, please call: (9) 617-_____

UNIT 8

UNIT 9

Town and country

Vocabulary

1 Label the pictures with the correct words.

> bus stop   bike lane   intersection   lamp post   ~~office building~~   traffic circle
> stop sign   apartment block   traffic lights   crosswalk

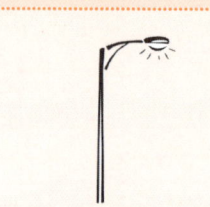

1. _office building_
2. _____ 
3. _____
4. _____ 
5. _____ 
6. _____ 
7. _____ 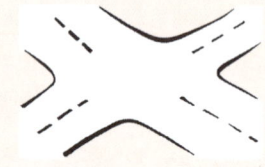
8. _____ 
9. _____ 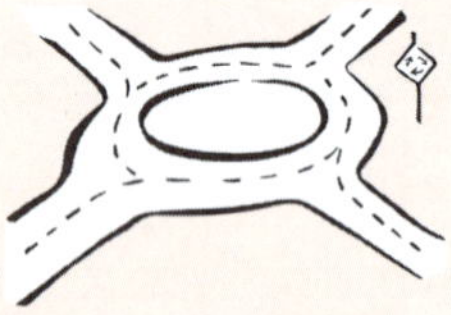
10. _____ 

2 Look at the picture and fill the blanks with the correct words.

> bridge   fence   hedge   sign   gate
> ~~path~~   field   stream

Run along the (1) _path_. On your left, there's a (2) _____ , and on your right, there's a (3) _____ . At the end of the path, there's a (4) _____ . Go through it. Don't forget to shut it so the moon cows can't get out of the (5) _____ . In front of you, you will see a (6) _____ with jumping fish in it. Don't put your hands or feet in the water. The fish are dangerous, and they might hurt you. To cross, go over the (7) _____ . On the other side, you will see a (8) _____ that says "TO THE SPACE STATION."

Dialogue work

3 Complete the dialogue with the correct words.

> fun   ham   night   not   oven   ~~party~~
> plates   plenty   trouble   walk

Eloisa What was your dad's birthday (1) _party_ like?

Jon It was (2) _____ , but we had a little trouble with the food.

Eloisa What do you mean? What kind of (3) _____ ?

Jon Well, in the morning, Mom put lots of cold chicken and (4) _____ on big plates. Then we all went out for a (5) _____ .

Eloisa And what happened?

Jon When we got back, there was nothing on the (6) _____ , and Perkins, our cat, looked really happy.

Eloisa You're joking.

Jon No, I'm (7) _____ . Perkins had eaten everything.

Eloisa What did you do?

Jon There was (8) _____ of other food to eat.

Eloisa What about the birthday cake? You were making it last (9) _____ when I called.

Jon We couldn't eat it.

Eloisa Why not?

Jon Because I'd forgotten to turn on the (10) _____ , so it wasn't cooked!

5 Fill the blanks with a verb in the past perfect simple.

> drink   not play   lose   not finish   ~~rain~~
> not fly   make   throw   not wash

1. The grass was wet because it _had rained_ in the night.
2. I asked Sara for the magazine, but she _____ it away.
3. I was scared on the plane because I _____ before.
4. There wasn't any orange juice because Gabe _____ it all.

Grammar practice

> There is a list of irregular past participles on page 136 of the Student's Book.

4 Match each sentence beginning to the correct ending. Put the verbs in brackets in the past perfect simple.

1. [f] I borrowed some money because _I had spent all mine._
2. [ ] His room was a mess because _____
3. [ ] I didn't sleep because _____
4. [ ] They lost the game because _____
5. [ ] The house was dark because _____
6. [ ] We didn't recognize her because _____
7. [ ] He forgot his lines in the play because _____
8. [ ] She was upset because _____

a) she (have) a fight with her best friend
b) I (drink) three cups of coffee
c) she (cut) her hair
d) they (not practice) enough
e) everyone (go) out
f) ~~I (spend) all mine~~
g) he (not learn) them very well
h) he (not clean) it for a week

5. I didn't win the tennis game because I _____ for a long time.
6. They climbed through the window because they _____ the keys.
7. We ate all the sandwiches that Melissa _____ for us.
8. The dog was really dirty because I _____ him for six months.
9. I didn't go to the play on Monday night because I _____ my history homework.

UNIT 9

6 Write sentences in the past perfect simple.

1. Andrea didn't want to go to a restaurant.
   (She / just / eat / a sandwich)
   She had just eaten a sandwich.

2. I saw Milly Bennett last week.
   (She / not change)
   _____

3. We arrived at the movie theater late.
   (We / miss / the first ten minutes)
   _____

4. There was water everywhere.
   (He / not turn off / the faucet)
   _____

5. Amy wasn't at home.
   (She / go / swimming)
   _____

6. My mother and I went to see *Titanic*.
   (She / not see / it)
   _____

7. Toby was hungry.
   (Nobody / give / him / his dinner)
   _____

7 Fill the blanks with *say/said* or *tell/told*.

1. Mark _said_ he was hungry.
2. What did he _tell_ you?
3. Did Sylvia _____ she'd be back by nine?
4. Josh _____ me he had a sore throat.
5. Please don't _____ Anna about the party.
6. I'll _____ you a secret about my little brother.
7. Did Lisa _____ she was going to the concert?
8. Mrs. Stanton _____ she didn't like dogs.
9. Did that man _____ you he was a policeman?
10. Joe asked us about the letter, but we didn't _____ him anything.
11. Justin asked me about Sandra, but I didn't _____ anything.
12. Please don't _____ me another stupid joke.

8 Report what young actor Dinesh Kumar said in a recent interview.

1. I really enjoy being an actor.
2. I meet lots of interesting people.
3. Last year, I was in a movie about skateboarders.
4. I had skateboarding lessons every day.
5. I can skateboard really well now.
6. I'm going to India in September to make a movie.
7. I'll be there for about six months.
8. I have lots of cousins in India.
9. My parents are going to visit me.
10. I'm not looking forward to the plane trip.
11. I don't like flying very much.

1. _He said he really enjoyed being an actor._
2. _____
3. _____
4. _____
5. _____
6. _____
7. _____
8. _____
9. _____
10. _____
11. _____

9 Write what Aunt Agatha and Megan said about their trip to the museum.

Aunt Agatha:
1. Megan took me to the piano museum.
2. Megan really enjoyed herself.
3. Megan loves going to museums.
4. Our visit wasn't long enough.
5. I can't wait to go there again with Megan.

Megan:
1. I went to the piano museum with my great aunt.
2. It was really boring.
3. I don't like looking at old things.
4. We spent hours there.
5. I'll never go out with Aunt Agatha again.

1. Aunt Agatha said <u>Megan had taken her to the piano museum.</u>
   Megan said <u>she had been to the piano museum with her great aunt.</u>
2. Aunt Agatha said _____
   Megan said _____
3. Aunt Agatha said _____
   Megan said _____
4. Aunt Agatha said _____
   Megan said _____
5. Aunt Agatha said _____
   Megan said _____

> Remember that *go* has two past participles: *been* and *gone*. See page 22 of this book and page 35 of the Student's Book.

10 Complete the sentences with verbs in the past perfect.

1. If I <u>'d had</u> (have) my camera, I would have taken a picture.
2. We'd have met you at the airport if you _____ (call) us.
3. If you _____ (not go) swimming in that lake, you wouldn't have gotten sick.
4. Mrs. Dalton wouldn't have been so angry if we _____ (clean) the room.
5. Toby would have eaten your dinner if I _____ (not stop) him.
6. If we _____ (have) a map, we wouldn't have gotten lost.
7. I wouldn't have gotten the main part in the school play if Jeremy _____ (not be) sick.

11 Complete the sentences in the third conditional.

1. The party <u>would have been</u> (be) okay if there'd been some good music.
2. If you'd called, we _____ (not be) so worried.
3. You _____ (get) a better grade if you'd done more work.
4. If you'd seen her face, you _____ (not laugh).
5. I _____ (call) you if I'd had my cell phone with me.
6. If I'd remembered her birthday, I _____ (send) her a card.
7. She _____ (not cut) her hand if she'd been more careful.
8. If we'd known about the party, we _____ (not go) to the movies.
9. You _____ (hurt) yourself if you'd dived in there.

Skills Development

Reading

1 Read the article. Where should these phrases go? Write them in the correct spaces.

- that has made a lot of people famous.
- dreamed of being a star
- she had her first big hit.
- I lost my friends.
- to be on a show.

Little girl with a big voice

Christina Aguilera (1) _____ _____ when she was only three. She used to put a towel on the floor as her stage, stand on it, and sing through a stick that she called her "icaphone"—microphone. Now she's one of the biggest names in pop, and Christina loves it. But life hasn't always been easy for her.

Christina Maria Aguilera was born on December 18, 1980, in Staten Island, New York. Her father, Fausto Aguilera, an Ecuadorian-American, was in the U.S. **army**, so the family moved around a lot. "It was difficult for me," says Christina, "because we didn't stay in the same place very long. We lived in New Jersey, Texas, and Japan. Every time we moved, (2) _____ . I'm still a bit jealous of people who have had the same best friend since they were little." Christina's parents divorced when she was fairly young, and she lived with her mother. She spent her teenage years in Wexford, Pennsylvania.

At the age of eight, she was on a TV show called *Star Search*. Christina soon discovered the disadvantages of being a **celebrity**. Christina's mom, Shelly, says, "Sometimes she missed school (3) _____ . Some of the kids at her school didn't like that. They were **mean** to her because she was different. In the end, we moved."

At twelve, Christina got a part on the *Mickey Mouse Club*, a TV show (4) _____ _____ . She was on it for the next two years, along with two other people who are now big names—Britney Spears and Justin Timberlake. While she was on the *Mickey Mouse Club* show, Christina felt very **lonely** at school. "I wanted to have friends and be like everyone else," she says. "I wanted to be a normal kid. But people get jealous of your success, and it creates problems."

The difficulties made Christina work harder at her music. She says, "I think that's why I **focused** on my career. My dream of becoming a recording artist helped me." Christina's **talent** and energy were recognized by the world very soon. When she was still only eighteen, (5) _____ _____ . *Genie In A Bottle* came out in 1999. It went to the top, and the rest is history!

2 Write T (true) or F (false).

1 Christina wasn't interested in singing when she was younger. ___
2 When she was a child, her family moved often. ___
3 She has had the same best friend all her life. ___
4 She was on TV when she was a young child. ___
5 She didn't have many friends at school. ___
6 She became successful when she was still a teenager. ___

Vocabulary

3a Match the words to the meanings.

1 celebrity   a) needing a friend
2 mean   b) famous person
3 lonely   c) give all your time and energy
4 focus   d) another word for *unkind*

3b Guess the meanings of these words, then check in a dictionary and write the translation.

army _____   talent _____

Listening

4 Listen to a conversation between Rosie and her mother and complete the sentences.

Rosie's friend Sophie had agreed to (1) _spend the night_ at her house. Sophie said she would bring (2) _____ . Then Sophie called and said she (3) _____ because she had to baby-sit (4) _____ . Rosie got annoyed because Sophie didn't sound very (5) _____ . If Sophie had called in the morning, Rosie could have (6) _____ else. Or she could have gone to (7) _____ with Erin.

Writing

5 Write about an argument you had with a friend. Use the sentences in Exercise 4 as a model. Start like this.

My friend _____ had agreed to
_____
_____

Study Tip

6 Your English will improve if you know your mistakes. Write down the two mistakes that you make most often in English. If you aren't sure, ask your teacher.

I forget the -s in the present simple (he knows, she says, etc.).

1 _____
_____

2 _____
_____

UNIT 9

UNIT 9

Talk Time

1 Complete the sentences with these phrases.

- a little
- finally
- isn't that
- see if
- something's happened
- right away

1 Please call us _____ when you arrive.
2 I have an extra ticket. Let's _____ Jen wants to come.
3 I've just gotten a letter from Sandra— _____ !
4 Look, Tanya—_____ David Beckham in that shop?
5 Why is everyone standing around the gate? I think _____ in the park.
6 You're looking _____ pale. Do you want to sit down?

2 Complete the e-mail with these phrases.

- especially
- I can show you around
- I can't wait!
- I'm looking forward to seeing you
- I hope that's okay

Send Mail: Message Composition

Hi Julio,
My parents will meet you at the airport on Friday morning.
(1) _____ with you. I can't come because I'll still be in school. But (2) _____ _____ Phoenix on Saturday and Sunday. Unfortunately, I have another two days of school on Monday and Tuesday, and then it's summer vacation.
(3) _____ On Wednesday morning, we're driving to California for a week. You're going to love California, (4) _____ the surfing.
(5) _____ again.
Dan

Let's Check

Vocabulary check

1 Match the words to the clues.

> bus stop   intersection   ~~office building~~   sidewalk
> traffic circle   sign   traffic lights   crosswalk

1. It's a tall building where people work. _office building_
2. Cars don't go on it, but people walk on it. _____
3. You wait here for a bus. _____
4. You cross the road here. _____
5. When they're red, the cars stop. When they're green, the cars go. _____
6. You'll see a _____ that says, "To The Zoo."
7. Go around the _____ and take the second exit.
8. When you get to the _____ , don't go left or right. Go straight.

Grammar check

2 Correct the mistake in each sentence.

> ◆ = there's a word missing
> N = change the order of two words
> X = change one word
> * = delete one word

1. You told that she couldn't do it. **X**
   You said that she couldn't do it.
2. He said that he broken his leg. ◆
   _____
3. If you'd been there, what you would have done? **N**
   _____
4. He said he will lend me his soccer cleats, but he didn't. **X**
   _____
5. They wouldn't have been worried if you would had called them. *
   _____

3 Choose the correct words for each sentence.

1. If I ___ in a hurry, I'd have gone to the café with them.
   A wasn't   **B** hadn't been (circled)   **C** wasn't being
2. When you arrived, we ___ finished eating.
   A already   **B** have already   **C** had already
3. I stayed in bed until 11:30 because I ___ to bed at 3:00 in the morning.
   A had gone   **B** have gone   **C** go
4. Jo ___ him that she was going out.
   A said   **B** told   **C** is telling
5. If you hadn't left the door open, the parrot ___ out.
   A didn't get   **B** wouldn't have   **C** wouldn't get gotten
6. Jim said he ___ interested in classical music.
   A wasn't   **B** wouldn't   **C** didn't
7. We couldn't get a room at the hotel because we ___ reserved one.
   A didn't   **B** hadn't   **C** weren't
8. You said you ___ write to me.
   A are   **B** would   **C** will
9. We'd have visited them if we ___ their address.
   A didn't lose   **B** haven't lost   **C** hadn't lost

4 Make sentences by putting the words in order. Add commas where necessary.

1. a / ham / Cathy / didn't / said / sandwich / she / want
   Cathy said she didn't want a ham sandwich.
2. because / favorite / had / her / lost / Natasha / ring / she / upset / was
   _____
3. couldn't / doctor / soccer / for / I / play / said / The / three weeks
   _____
4. been / everything / have / he'd / If / okay / said / he / was sorry / would
   _____

UNIT 9

UNIT 10 Eating out

Vocabulary

1 Match the words to the numbers.

salad plate _3_
bowl ___
soup spoon ___
fork ___
glass ___
pitcher ___
knife ___
napkin ___
pepper ___
plate ___
salt ___
saucer ___
cup ___
teaspoon ___

Dialogue work

2 Write the sentences in the correct order to make dialogues.

Dialogue 1
- Sam Forester.
- Can we order some drinks, please?
- Sure. What would you like?
- ~~We reserved a table for four.~~
- Could we have four glasses of lemonade?
- This is your table.
- What name, please?
- Yes. I'll get you those now.

Sam   _We reserved a table for four._
Waiter _____
Sam   _____
Waiter _____
Sam   _____
      _____
Waiter _____
Sam   _____
      _____
Waiter _____

Dialogue 2
- Anything else?
- ~~Are you ready to order now?~~
- One chicken salad, one hamburger with fries, and two pizzas.
- One large green salad, then.
- What would you like?
- Yes, please. Can we also have a large green salad?
- Yes, I think we are.

Waiter _Are you ready to order now?_
Sam   _____
Waiter _____
Sam   _____
      _____
Waiter _____
Sam   _____
      _____
Waiter _____

Grammar practice

3 Write sentences in the present perfect continuous with *for* or *since*.

1 They're talking on the phone. They started talking an hour ago.
They've been talking on the phone for an hour.

2 He's doing his homework. He started it at two o'clock.
_____
_____

3 We're biking around Europe. We started in June.
_____
_____

4 They're making a tree house. They started it weeks ago.
_____
_____

5 I'm writing a play. I started in September.
_____
_____

6 You're standing on your head. You started ten minutes ago.
_____
_____

7 She's testing. She started twenty minutes ago.
_____
_____

4 Write the verbs in the present perfect continuous.

1 Mom is in the kitchen. She *'s been cooking* (cook) since six o'clock this morning!

2 I'm tired because I _____ _____ (not sleep) well lately.

3 You look tired. What _____ _____ (you / do) all day?

4 I _____ (write) postcards all afternoon. This is the tenth one!

5 Seth _____ (wear) that silly hat all day. He looks ridiculous.

6 I can't find my keys. I _____ (look) for them all day.

7 You look red. How long _____ _____ (you / lie) in the sun?

5 Complete the sentences with a verb in the past simple passive.

> allow   make   give   leave   tell   invite   ~~take~~

1 This photo *was taken* when we were on vacation in Turkey last year.

2 We _____ a toothbrush, a comb, and some socks on the plane when we went to New York.

3 Simon and Jack _____ to Andy's party, but they couldn't go.

4 Why are you so late? You _____ to be here by nine.

5 This bracelet _____ by a friend who lives in Kenya.

6 This watch _____ in our bathroom last weekend. Whose is it?

7 I _____ to hold one of the lambs on Jon's farm. It was so cute.

- We use *for* when we're talking about a period of time.
  She's been talking **for** 20 minutes.
  We've been living here **for** three months.
- We use *since* when we give the beginning of the time.
  She's been talking **since** two o'clock.
  We've been living here **since** January.

6 Match the beginnings to the endings. Write sentences in the past simple passive.

1. [d] My sneakers (not made)
2. [ ] We (not allow)
3. [ ] She (not hurt) very badly
4. [ ] We (not meet) when
5. [ ] I (not tell)
6. [ ] The poor dog (not take)
7. [ ] You (not expect) to do

a) about Carly's accident
b) all the dishes
c) for a walk yesterday
d) ~~in Korea~~
e) we arrived at the airport
f) to stay up late last Thursday
g) when she fell off her bike

1. *My sneakers weren't made in Korea.*
2. _____
3. _____
4. _____
5. _____
6. _____
7. _____

7 Use the prompts to write questions in the simple past passive.

1. (you / invite) to Anita's last party?
   Were you invited to Anita's last party?
2. Where (the money / find)?
   _____
3. How many plates (break) at the party?
   _____
4. (*Hamlet* / write) by Shakespeare?
   _____
5. When (the telephone / invent)?
   _____
6. What time (breakfast / serve) yesterday?
   _____
7. (anyone / hurt) in the accident?
   _____
8. Why (the windows / leave) open?
   _____
9. (these plates / wash) in the dishwasher or by hand?
   _____

8 Report the questions that each person asked you.

Speech bubbles:
- When are you going to take out the trash?
- Why did you miss soccer practice on Saturday?
- Who did you dance with at Sara's party?
- Where is your project?
- How did you twist your ankle?
- How many times have you practiced this week?
- What have you bought for Dad's birthday?

1 My doctor asked me _how I had twisted my ankle._
2 My Geography teacher asked me _____
3 My mother asked me _____
4 The soccer coach asked me _____
5 My best friend asked me _____
6 My little sister asked me _____
7 My piano teacher asked me _____

9 Report the questions that you asked each person.

1 Holly, are you busy?
   I asked Holly if she was busy.

2 Justin, do you like spicy food?
   _____

3 Julia, can you remember the address?
   _____

4 Lynn, will you be ready in an hour?
   _____

5 Nick, are your parents coming to the game?
   _____

6 Ben, are you going to write to Rosie?
   _____

7 Erica, did you see the baby elephants at the zoo?
   _____

CULTURE SPOT

THE MOST POPULAR FOOD IN THE U.S.

Tacos are getting more popular and everybody loves pizza, but hamburgers are still America's favorite fast food. Americans have been eating hamburgers for more than 75 years. But we still don't know the true origin of the burger.

One story is that the first hamburger was sold in Seymour, Wisconsin, in 1885. A fifteen-year-old named Charlie Nagreen was selling meatballs at a market. But no one bought them because they were too messy to eat. Charlie made the meatballs flat and put them between two slices of bread. He called them "hamburgers" and sold them at the same market every year until he died in 1951. Other people say a man named Louis Lassen made the first hamburger. A customer in his New Haven, Connecticut, restaurant wanted a fast meal. Louis made a quick sandwich of ground beef between two slices of bread. But these two stories don't explain one thing. How did ground-beef sandwiches get the name of "**ham**burgers"?

Perhaps we have to look at a third story. Apparently in 1891, sailors from the U.S. visited Hamburg, Germany, and ate sandwiches there made of ground beef with egg on top. They liked the sandwich, and when they got back to America, they asked cooks in New York to make it for them.

We'll probably never be sure of the origin of the hamburger. But we do know that it became very popular in the 1940s. More and more Americans at that time were buying cars and driving around the country. A few small restaurants realized that people wanted food quickly while they were on the road. By the 1950s, nearly everyone in the U.S. was eating hamburgers.

These days, Americans eat billions of hamburgers a year. On average, each person buys about three hamburgers a week. Teenage boys probably eat more hamburgers than anyone. They eat out several times a week, and when they eat out, most of them eat hamburgers!

There are many different toppings for hamburgers, but most people like lettuce, tomato, pickles, ketchup, and cheese. The most common thing to eat with hamburgers is French fries, but a lot of restaurants also serve side orders of potato chips, onion rings, and salad.

Fourteen-year-old Delara Thomas says, "I love burgers with loads of mustard and pickles. We have them every Saturday. I go to the gym for a swim, and when I get home, my dad has burgers waiting on the grill. We eat them with French fries and a milkshake. I know it's a greasy meal, but I don't mind once a week. I hate onion rings. They make your breath stink!"

Reading

1 Read the text and answer the questions.

1 Why didn't anyone want Charlie Nagreen's meatballs at first?
   _____
   _____

2 Where did Louis Lassen work?
   _____
   _____

3 What were the sandwiches like that some U.S. soldiers tried in Hamburg?
   _____
   _____

4 Why did hamburgers become so popular in the 1940s?
   _____
   _____
   _____

5 How many hamburgers does each person buy on average every week in the U.S.?
   _____
   _____

6 What do most people eat on their hamburgers?
   _____
   _____
   _____

Vocabulary

2 Find the words for:

1 a green vegetable used in salad _____
2 a cold tomato sauce _____
3 a portion of food that is not the main course _____
4 an O-shaped fried vegetable _____
5 a peppery yellow sauce _____
6 an ice-cream drink _____
7 full of oil or fat _____
8 smell bad _____

Project

3 Write about you and food.

1 Who usually cooks in your family?
   _____

2 What's your favorite food?
   _____

3 Do you enjoy cooking?
   _____

4 What can you cook?
   _____
   _____

5 What kind of foreign food is popular in your country?
   _____
   _____

6 Do you have a favorite restaurant? What kind of food can you get there?
   _____
   _____
   _____

7 What's the most popular fast food in your country?
   _____
   _____

8 Is there any food that you don't like?
   _____

9 Is anyone in your family a vegetarian?
   _____

10 What's a typical meal in your family?
   _____

Study Tip

Writing interesting sentences

You can use words like *but*, *because*, *until*, *as* and *while* to join your ideas together.

Look at these pairs of sentences.
He sold hamburgers at the same market every year.
He died in 1951.

No one bought the meatballs.
They were too messy to eat.

Now look at how you can join them.
He sold hamburgers at the same market every year until he died in 1951.

No one bought the meatballs because they were too messy to eat.

When you're reading, notice how these words are used. Then try to use them in your own writing.

UNIT 10

Listening

1 What do they all think of fast food? Listen and write the correct letter in each box.

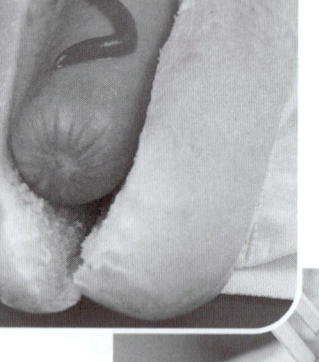

a) boring ~~b) cheap~~ c) delicious d) quick
e) spicy f) unhealthy g) unusual

1. Mark — b
2. Zoe ☐
3. Adam ☐
4. Melanie ☐
5. Sam ☐

2a Which restaurant does the Walker family decide to go to? Look at the ads, listen, and check (✔) the correct box.

A ☐ **The Texas Burger** — We can arrange birthday parties.

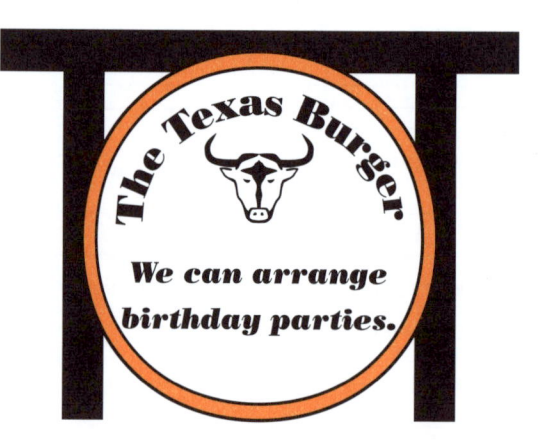

B ☐ **The Light of Nepal** — Fine Indian food. Vegetarian dishes available.

C ☐ **The Green Room** — Thai cooking. Try our Sunday lunch menu for only $12

2b Why do they choose it? Write three reasons.

They choose it because …

1. _____
2. _____
3. _____

Let's Check

Vocabulary check

1 The first and last letter are missing from each of these words. They are all things you can see on a dining-room table.

1. s_ou_p s_poo_n
2. __nif__
3. __or__
4. __easpoo__
5. __lat__
6. __ow__
7. __apki__
8. __las__
9. __auce__
10. __al__
11. __eppe__

2 Fill in the blanks with the correct words.

| burned | ~~cup~~ | overdone | pitcher | delicious | spicy |

1. Would you like another _cup_ of coffee?
2. I'm afraid the cake is completely _____. We can't eat it. It's all black on top.
3. That was a _____ meal. Thank you very much.
4. If you want milk in your coffee, help yourself. There's a _____ of it on the table.
5. Do you like Indian food? It's pretty _____.
6. I've cooked the fish a little too much. I'm afraid it's _____.

Grammar check

3 Correct the mistake in each sentence.

- ♦ = there's a word missing
- X = change one word
- N = change the order of two words
- * = delete one word

1. How long you been waiting? ♦
   How long have you been waiting?
2. I asked him where was he staying. N
   _____
3. She has playing cards for hours. ♦
   _____
4. Where was these earrings found? X
   _____
5. Did you ask him he knew Pedro? ♦
   _____
6. I was been told to wait here for them. *
   _____

4 Choose the correct words for each sentence.

1. These chocolates ___ given to me last weekend.
   A was   **B were** (circled)   C aren't
2. I asked him ___ happy at his new school.
   A that he was   B he was   C if he was
3. Cathy asked me if she ___ borrow my bike.
   A does   B will   C could
4. How long ___ she been living in Spain?
   A was   B did   C has
5. Ruth asked me what ___ doing at Christmas.
   A I was   B will I   C I will
6. We ___ to the station by bus.
   A took us   B were taken   C were taking
7. This purse ___ found in the school bathrooms yesterday.
   A was   B is   C were
8. The cat ___ been watching the hamster all day.
   A has   B is   C was
9. They asked me if I ___ like to have lunch with them.
   A did   B will   C would
10. This cake ___ by my sister.
    A was making   B was made   C were made
11. They ___ been eating cookies all day.
    A have   B did   C were

5 Make sentences by putting the words in order. Add commas where necessary.

1. any / given / lunch / We / weren't
   We weren't given any lunch.
2. asked / hadn't / he / him / Mom / called / why
   _____
3. been / classes / dance / going / haven't / I / my / to
   _____
4. pillows / backyard / in / left / the / these / were / Why / ?
   _____
5. asked / floor / her / I / on / she / sleeping / the / was / why
   _____

UNIT **10**

Practice

The South African swimmer Natalie Dutoit has always been a very determined person. When she was a child, she suffered from asthma. Her parents decided that swimming would be good for her health and took her to swimming lessons at the age of six. Natalie didn't like swimming at first. She was scared of water and held onto the side of the pool. But she wanted to learn to swim, and she didn't give up. Little by little, she became more confident, and, by the age of ten, she was breaking all the records for her age group. By the age of fourteen, she was one of South Africa's most promising young swimmers.

But when she was eighteen, Natalie had a serious scooter accident. Her left leg was very badly injured, and doctors had to amputate it at the knee. Natalie showed great courage and determination after the accident. Most people take a year to learn to walk with an artificial leg, but Natalie practiced in the hospital hallway and was walking in five hours. She started swimming again just six weeks after the accident. And just eighteen months after the accident, Natalie took part in the Commonwealth Games at Manchester, England. She broke two world records and won gold medals in the 50-meter and 100-meter disabled freestyle swimming events. She also got into the finals of the 800-meter freestyle event for able-bodied swimmers.

Now nineteen-year-old Natalie's goal is to compete against able-bodied swimmers in the next Olympics. "I'm still the same person, and I can reach the same goals," she says. Natalie, who believes people can learn from every experience in life, says she does get sad sometimes, but she doesn't want pity. She says the best thing for her mood is to get into the water. "I'm not sociable," she says, "and in the water I can get away from everyone."

Natalie is not just a great swimmer. She is also an excellent speaker who fights for the rights of disabled people in South Africa and the rest of the world. She says governments should make it easier for disabled people to study, get jobs, and do sports. Her determination to overcome her own problems will certainly give courage to other people.

Reading

1 Read the text and answer the questions.

1 Where does Natalie Dutoit come from?
   _____
2 What was Natalie's problem when she was a child?
   _____
3 At what age did she start going to a swimming pool?
   _____
   _____
4 Did she enjoy swimming right from the start?
   _____
5 What happened to Natalie when she was eighteen?
   _____
   _____
6 How long after the accident did she start swimming again?
   _____
   _____
7 Why did she have to learn to walk again after the accident?
   _____
   _____
8 What did she achieve at the Commonwealth Games in Manchester?
   _____
   _____
9 What does Natalie want to do in the next Olympics?
   _____
   _____
10 What helps Natalie most when she feels sad?
   _____
11 Do you like competitive sports? Why or why not?
   _____
   _____
12 What do you think about Natalie Dutoit? Finish this sentence: In my opinion, She's...
   _____

2 Read the text again. Check the statement (A–C) that best sums up the most important points for each paragraph.

Paragraph 1
A Natalie Dutoit started swimming at the age of six, but she didn't enjoy it. ☐
B Natalie Dutoit did not enjoy swimming at first, but by fourteen she had become one of South Africa's top swimmers. ☐
C Natalie Dutoit used to suffer from asthma, so her parents made her start swimming lessons at the age of six. ☐

Paragraph 2
A At eighteen, she was in a scooter accident and lost a leg. ☐
B At eighteen, she lost a leg in a scooter accident, but she is still a champion swimmer. ☐
C After losing a leg in a scooter accident, she had to learn to walk with an artificial leg. ☐

Paragraph 3
A Natalie wants to compete in the next Olympics and doesn't want people to feel sorry for her. ☐
B Natalie says she still has a lot to learn. ☐
C Natalie now swims to escape from other people. ☐

Paragraph 4
A Natalie is a great swimmer and a good speaker. ☐
B Natalie is a great swimmer and has a lot of energy. ☐
C Natalie is a great swimmer who does her best to help other disabled people. ☐

Test Paper

Nobody is entirely sure of the origins of ice cream. We do know that 2,000 years ago, Alexander the Great enjoyed eating snow and ice, flavored with honey. We also know that three hundred years later, the Roman emperor Nero used to send his workers into the mountains to get snow, which was then mixed with fruit juices. It's hard to imagine how they could bring the snow back to the hot city before it melted, but somehow they succeeded. Nero even had special cold rooms under his palace where he could keep the snow to make his cold fruit juices.

But we can't really call those early snowy drinks ice cream, can we? We have to wait until the thirteenth century when something more like ice cream reached Europe. Luckily for us, in 1295, the Venetian traveler Marco Polo returned from China with recipes for water ices, or sorbets—iced desserts made with honey, fruit, and syrup.

By the seventeenth century, "cream ice," as it was called, had reached the court of the English king Charles I. By now it really was a kind of ice cream, made with cream and milk, rather than a sorbet or water ice.

Ice cream reached America in the eighteenth century. But it was still only for the very rich. It used to take a huge effort to make it. You needed lots of ice and a cold room to keep it in. And it took at least 40 minutes of shaking and stirring the mixture by hand. President George Washington spent $200 on ice cream during the summer of 1790.

Until the nineteenth century, ice cream was only made at home. But in 1851, the world's first ice-cream factory was opened in Baltimore, and soon everyone in America was eating ice cream.

It was another 45 years before an Italian immigrant to America, Italo Marchiony, invented ice-cream cones. Marchiony had an ice-cream stall on Wall Street in New York. He used to sell homemade ice cream in little glasses. But he was losing money because a lot of his customers used to break or keep the ice-cream glasses. So he made thin pastry cups, or cones, that people could eat, and he served his ice cream in them. Marco Polo would have been impressed!

Reading

1 Read the text and answer the questions.

1 What was Alexander the Great's iced drink like?
   _____
   _____

2 How did Nero's workers make his ice dessert?
   _____
   _____

3 Where was Nero's supply of snow kept?
   _____
   _____

4 Where did Marco Polo get his recipes for water ices?
   _____
   _____

5 When did people start to eat ice cream in America?
   _____
   _____

6 How much was George Washington's ice-cream bill in 1790?
   _____
   _____

7 When was the first ice-cream factory opened?
   _____
   _____

8 What did Italo Marchiony invent?
   _____
   _____

9 Why did he need his new invention?
   _____
   _____

10 Would you like to work in the food industry? Why/Why not?
   _____
   _____
   _____

11 Describe your ideal meal in three sentences.
   _____
   _____
   _____
   _____

Writing

2 Write a letter to your American pen pal. Include the following:

- Tell him/her about a birthday meal at a restaurant last week. Say whose birthday it was and who was at the restaurant. Describe what you ate at the meal.
- Ask two questions about his/her birthday party last month.
- Tell him/her one of your plans for summer vacation.
- Ask about his/her plans for summer vacation.
- Invite him/her to visit you during the vacation.
- Describe two things you would like to do with your friend if he/she visits in the summer.

Write between 80 and 100 words.

Dear _____
_____
_____
_____
_____
_____
_____
_____
_____
_____
_____
_____
_____
_____
_____
_____
_____
_____

Looking forward to hearing from you.

Best wishes,

_____

3 Read the article about the invention of the movies. Are the sentences right (A) or wrong (B)? If there is not enough information to answer "Right" or "Wrong," choose "Doesn't say" (C).

The Lumière Brothers

The movies were born in France on December 28, 1895. That's the day when Auguste and Louis Lumière gave the first public movie show to a paying audience. The show, which lasted only twenty minutes in total, took place in the basement of a café in Paris. There were ten short films showing moving images from everyday life. One movie showed workers leaving a factory. Another one showed a train coming toward the camera. A lot of people in the audience screamed and ran out of the movie theater when they saw it. They thought it was a real train that was crashing into the café.

To show their movies, the Lumière brothers used a machine called a "cinematographe." It was a camera and projector in one. It was fairly light and weighed only about five kilos. This allowed them to move it around easily.

By 1900, the Lumières had made over 1,000 short movies. But strangely, Louis Lumière was not very confident about his invention. He said, "The movies are an invention without a future." He thought that people would get bored of images that they could easily see when they went for a walk down the street.

1 The first public movie show took place in Paris in 1995.
   A Right   **B** Wrong (circled)   **C** Doesn't say

2 The show lasted twenty minutes.
   A Right   **B** Wrong   **C** Doesn't say

3 The movies showed actors performing in a silent story.
   A Right   **B** Wrong   **C** Doesn't say

4 The audience paid one franc to watch.
   A Right   **B** Wrong   **C** Doesn't say

5 Some people were scared during the show.
   A Right   **B** Wrong   **C** Doesn't say

6 The Lumière brothers' movie camera was not very heavy.
   A Right   **B** Wrong   **C** Doesn't say

7 A lot of workers helped the Lumières with their filming.
   A Right   **B** Wrong   **C** Doesn't say

8 The Lumière brothers also made one long movie.
   A Right   **B** Wrong   **C** Doesn't say

9 Louis Lumière was sure that the movies would become very popular one day.
   A Right   **B** Wrong   **C** Doesn't say

4 Read the article about superstition. Choose the best word (A, B, or C) for each space.

Superstition

(1) ___ you believe in luck? Do you (2) ___ a lucky number? Or a lucky color? If you answered "yes" to one (3) ___ those questions, then you are probably superstitious. (4) ___ worry about it. Around 25% of people in the U.S. admit that they are (5) ___ little superstitious.

Superstitions exist in (6) ___ country, but they aren't always (7) ___ same. For example, in the U.S., people (8) ___ on wood for luck. But in Italy, it's lucky (9) ___ touch iron. In Britain and the U.S., the number thirteen is (10) ___ unlucky. (11) ___ there an unlucky number in your country?

1	**A** Are	**B** Do (circled)	**C** Does
2	**A** choose	**B** your	**C** have
3	**A** of	**B** for	**C** from
4	**A** Shouldn't	**B** Don't	**C** Stop
5	**A** some	**B** a	**C** just
6	**A** all	**B** most	**C** every
7	**A** the	**B** for	**C** your
8	**A** knocking	**B** knocked	**C** knock
9	**A** for	**B** to	**C** if
10	**A** too	**B** the	**C** very
11	**A** Is	**B** Was	**C** Has

5 Read the information and complete the application form.

Carmen Sánchez is from Bilbao, in Spain. She's twenty years old, and she's studying tourism at the University of Miami. She's lived in Florida for two years and is now fluent in English. She spent a year in France when she was fifteen and speaks French. She loves sports, especially swimming, tennis, and volleyball. She learned to windsurf three years ago, but she has never worked in a water-sports school.

Lagoon Water Sports Application Form
Name: (1) *Carmen Sánchez*
Nationality: (2) _____
Age: (3) _____
Occupation: (4) _____
Foreign languages: (5) _____
How long have you been in Florida?
(6) _____
Favorite sports: (7) _____
_____
Have you ever taught windsurfing? (8) _____

Listening

6 You will hear some information about movies at the Laguna Movie Theater. Listen and complete the information. You will hear the information twice.

Laguna Movie Theater Recorded Information

Date: Monday (1) _____
Screen 1: *Electric* (2) _____
    showing at (3) _____ and 7:30
Screen 2: *Don't Look* (4) _____
    showing at 5:35 and (5) _____
Adults pay (6) _____
Children under 12 pay (7) _____
Students pay (8) _____
The café has a selection of sodas, sandwiches, and (9) _____. The Laguna Movie Theater is on (10) _____ Street.
To reserve tickets, call: 352-430-(11) _____

7 Listen to Jessie and Alice talking about Jessie's birthday presents. What did each person give Jessie? Write a letter a–i next to each person.

PEOPLE **PRESENTS**

1 Uncle David [h]   a) watch   g) video
2 Mom   [ ]   b) candle   h) book
3 Dad   [ ]   c) CD   i) bracelet
4 Mark   [ ]   d) mask
5 Sara   [ ]   e) pen
6 Alice   [ ]   f) socks

8 Listen to six short conversations and check (✔) the right answer.

1 What time is it?
   A 4:45 ☐   B 5:15 ✔   C 5:30 ☐

2 How much is the magazine?
   A $1.50 ☐   B $2.15 ☐   C $2.50 ☐

3 When is Ella going to Wichita?
   A 8/13 ☐   B 8/3 ☐   C 8/30 ☐

4 How is she traveling to Kansas?
   A (train) ☐   B (plane) ☐   C (bus) ☐

5 Where are the socks?
   A ☐   B ☐   C ☐

6 What time is the class?
   A 2:15 ☐   B 2:05 ☐   C 2:50 ☐

Macmillan Education
Between Towns Road, Oxford OX4 3PP
A division of Macmillan Publishers Limited
Companies and representatives throughout the world

ISBN 978 1 4050 2323 8

© 2004 Edumond Le Monnier SpA, Milano, Italy
Text © Olivia Johnston 2004
Design and illustration © Macmillan Publishers Limited 2004

First published 2004

All rights reserved; no part of this publication may be reproduced,
stored in a retrieval system, transmitted in any form, or by any means,
electronic, mechanical, photocopying, recording, or otherwise, without
the prior written permission of the publishers.

Designed by Victory Productions, Inc.
Illustrated by Katherine Anderson, Mike Cucurullo, Michelle Gawe, Peter Kelly, Dana Mardaga, Ruth Pettis, Leticia Plate, Derek Ring
Cover design by Mackerel Limited
Cover photos by Rubberball Productions (L), Photodisc (R)

Authors' acknowledgements
The author would like to thank Mark Farrell for his support and advice, and Catriona Watson-Brown for her patience, energy, and eagle eye.

The authors and publishers would like to thank the following for permission to reproduce their photographs:
Alamy: Brand X Pictures p 60(r), Foodcollection.com p 86(r), GOODSHOOT p 68(tr), image100 pp 11(tl), 76, 77(b), images-of-france p 70(b), Jonathan Plant p 32(br); Corbis: Bettmann p 54, Macduff Everton p 50(tr), Kevin Fleming p 50(br), Dave G. Hauser pp 50(tl), 68(bl), Robert Holmes p 68(br), Jones Jon p 18, Layne Kennedy p 50(bl), LWA-Dann Tardiff p 11(bl), Tony Roberts p 68(tl), Royalty-Free pp 11(tr), 70(t), 86(l), Michael St. Maur Sheil p 60(l), Kim Sayer p 72, Sygma p 59(m), Frank Trapper p 78; Digital Vision p 77(t), 88(t,b); The Guide Horse Foundation p 42(t,b); Photodisc pp 11(br), 32 (t, c, bl), 34, 52, 59 (ml, mr, r), 60(ml), 92; Rubberball Productions p 6

Printed and bound in Thailand

2014 2013 2012 2011 2010
18 17 16 15 14